Standard Methods of

CLINICAL CHEMISTRY

VOLUME I

Standard Methods of
CLINICAL
CHEMISTRY

VOLUME I

BY THE AMERICAN ASSOCIATION
OF CLINICAL CHEMISTS

Editor-in-Chief:

MIRIAM REINER

Director, Chemistry Laboratory
Gallinger Municipal Hospital
Washington, D. C.

1953
ACADEMIC PRESS INC., *Publishers*
NEW YORK, N. Y.

ACADEMIC PRESS, INC.
111 Fifth Avenue, New York, New York 10003

United Kingdom Edition published by
ACADEMIC PRESS, INC. (LONDON) LTD.
Berkeley Square House, London W1X6BA

LIBRARY OF CONGRESS CATALOG CARD NUMBER: 53-7099

Fifth Printing, 1969

PRINTED IN THE UNITED STATES OF AMERICA

Preface

This is the first volume in the series of "Standard Methods of Clinical Chemistry" published by the American Association of Clinical Chemists. The method of issuing small volumes seems to be the best way of keeping the series up to date, as it will allow revisions from time to time without waiting to reissue all the methods.

The methods used every day in the clinical laboratory are of primary importance, since a laboratory can be no better than the methods it employs. That is the reason why in the first volume we have undertaken the study of some of the methods used most frequently and have left specialized subjects for later. The choice of the most important is always a difficult problem in any selection of methods. The exact order of importance of those chosen here may be debatable, but almost all laboratories include the analysis of these constituents in their daily repertoire.

With rapid advances being made in the fields of instrumentation and methodology, one cannot say how long the method submitted will be the one of choice; so, whenever necessary, future volumes will present supplementary procedures and modifications of the published methods. Whenever the analytical principle can be carried out in a variety of ways, one of them has been selected by the Submitter. This selection is based on the consensus of clinical chemists working with these methods daily in their own laboratories; this does not imply that other modifications may not be equally satisfactory.

The procedure is as follows: first, the method is well tested in the laboratory of the *Submitter;* then it is sent to the *Checkers,* who retest it in their own laboratories for its validity and practicality. Results, suggestions, and criticisms of the Checkers are incorporated in the method published by the Submitter. Such a procedure not only requires testing of the method but also includes checking a sufficient number of blood samples from control and pathological cases. This is time-consuming, but we feel that thorough checking

126073

of the method under practical conditions more than compensates for the time spent. After all, there are many excellent collections of biochemical procedures available, but although many of these methods yield excellent results when applied to a research problem, they may be impractical under the rigorous regime of a routine clinical chemical laboratory where speed and simplicity are next in importance to precision.

We have tried to elucidate the scientific basis of each method, its scope, and its limitations without engulfing it in unnecessary detail. The variation in the length of the chapters is due partly to the difference in the topics and partly to the treatment by the author. For example, the thymol turbidity test is comparatively new and empirical, whereas the determination of uric acid goes back as far as the beginning of biochemistry and has a real historical background.

To all members of the Editorial Committee, both past and present, I wish to convey my heartfelt thanks for their kind cooperation in a rather tedious job. I am sorry to record the untimely death of Jos Kahn, one of the staunch supporters of this project.

To Harry Sobotka and John G. Reinhold, presidents of the American Association of Clinical Chemists during the planning and writing of this book, I am deeply indebted for their generous support. It is a pleasure to thank Mrs. Peggy Richard for her assistance in typing the manuscript and Bernard H. Armbrecht for proofreading the manuscript.

This book has been written for the countless laboratory workers, chemists, and technicians who are such a vital part of the medical profession, who share in the work, but seldom in the glory. We hope that all who use this book will find it of service and will not hesitate to make suggestions. In this way we can judge the value of our project and extend its scope.

Washington, D. C.   MIRIAM REINER
May, 1953

Foreword

The present edition of "Standard Methods of Clinical Chemistry" represents one of the most cherished achievements of the American Association of Clinical Chemists. The Constitution of the Association, written in 1948, enumerates standardization and codification of methods among its foremost objectives in the interest of the public welfare. Successive Executive Committees of the Association have pondered over the best form for this task. It was decided to summarize the methods of clinical chemistry in a form similar to the "Official and Tentative Methods of Analysis" of the Association of Official Agricultural Chemists and the excellent presentation of "Organic Syntheses." It is hoped that volumes of the "Standard Methods," will accomplish this purpose by presenting individual methods, delineating the underlying principle, describing precisely the preparation of reagents and sequence of procedures, and indicating the range of normal and pathological results.

Quantitative clinical chemistry is less than a century old. One of its first exponents was J. L. W. Thudichum, that versatile scientist, who was by training a physician but who felt equally at home in the practice of wine-making, in writing the "Chemistry of the Brain" and the "Spirit of Cookery," and in studying problems of sanitation and the analytical methods of the hospital chemist. His lifetime coincides with the flourishing of cellular pathology and bacteriology, which has in turn made modern aseptic surgery possible. During this exciting period in the history of medicine, organic and physical chemistry developed their particular concepts which form the foundation of a well-organized science. The change in outlook and methodology from the secretive mystical craft of the alchemist to the logical and well-documented science of chemistry was more abrupt than the development of any other physical or biological discipline. It is little wonder that the great chemists during this heroic age considered the animal body as a source of interesting starting materials rather than as a primary object of their endeavors. Even now, half a century after biochemistry has developed as an independent specialty, one may imagine an invisible line of demarcation between biological chemists and others who should, perhaps, properly be called chemical biologists. The former are interested for instance in the mechanisms of glycolysis or the structure of proteins *per se*, whereas the latter consider the identical problems but with a view to their significance in animal and plant life and evolution.

How did the clinical chemist enter the picture? A treatise called "Der Blutzucker" was written in 1913 by Ivar Bang, M.D., of the University of Lund in Sweden. He proposed microtechniques, comparable to Pregl's microanalytical methods, for the expeditious analysis of small quantities of blood such as could be drawn daily from patients under investigation.. It is no mere coincidence that Bang was a doctor of medicine, like Ehrlich, the originator of both histochemistry and immunochemistry. But soon the impact of medicine upon chemistry became so significant that biochemists such as Folin and Benedict, van Slyke and Bloor dedicated themselves to the tasks of blood and urine analysis and created the structure of clinical chemistry.

Its methods have been described and collected in several scientific treatises which delve into the history and rationale of these procedures, and in publications by apparatus-makers who describe the techniques with reference to their specific product.

We speak to clinical chemists, technicians as well as supervisors. For historical reasons to which we have alluded, much clinical chemistry was originally carried out by doctors of medicine. For practical reasons it was natural that increasing specialization delegated the laboratory sciences to the pathologist's laboratory. The operation of flame photometers, electrophoretic equipment, microanalytical apparatus, and other machinery is gaining in importance, and this development is reflected in the steadily increasing employment by hospitals and private laboratories of competent and responsible clinical chemists. At present, much of the simpler clinical chemistry is performed by technicians, working, as it were, in isolated situations. We hope that they too will benefit from a perusal of "Standard Methods."

Considering the wide scope of clinical chemistry, its steady growth, and the progress of instrumentation, we have decided to issue this collection as a series of small volumes. This insures great flexibility and facilitates as far as possible the task of Editors, Submitters, and Checkers. At the same time, it permits the issuance of handy volumes for use at the laboratory bench, and the current presentation of new and timely methods and modifications. Grouping of certain methods in each book will provide a welcome opportunity of acquiring individual volumes for those interested in a specific subject.

We hope that "Standard Methods of Clinical Chemistry" will raise the standards of clinical chemistry and will ultimately improve the medical care of the population.

New York, New York   THE EDITORIAL COMMITTEE OF
                                          THE AMERICAN ASSOCIATION OF
                                          CLINICAL CHEMISTS.

Contents

Introduction

M. E. HODES

Lieutenant, Medical Corps, U. S. Naval Reserve; Head, Department of Physiological Chemistry, U. S. Naval Medical School, National Naval Medical Center, Bethesda, Maryland.*

Introduction

The clinical chemist is a professional member of the medical team responsible for the diagnosis of a patient's illness and for the therapy of his ailment. As such, he is responsible for the accurate performance and reporting of the laboratory procedures entrusted to him. The dosage of drugs such as dicumarol and insulin, pre- and post-operative management of fluid balance, and even the type of nutrition offered will depend on the results of chemical examination. The patient's welfare is as much the chemist's trust as that of the supervising physician.

The scope of the clinical chemist's responsibility varies in different institutions, but it may include any or all of the following:

1. Collection of specimens for analysis: This is often left to the intern; but when the chemist performs the task himself he is assured of adequate amounts and proper samples. He avoids the annoyance attendant upon receiving a request for serum potassium attached to a vial of blood preserved with potassium oxalate.

2. Performance of the test: This should be done as soon as possible after collection of the sample. The test then will not only nearly mirror the physiological state of the patient at the time of reporting the result (when it is of most use to the physician) but will also assure that the changes that occur in blood on standing have been minimized. For instance, a report of the blood sugar, serum chloride, and carbon dioxide combining power of blood tested several hours after collection will reveal a low sugar and carbon dioxide and

---

* Present address: Cell Chemistry Laboratory, Department of Biochemistry, College of Physicians and Surgeons, Columbia University, New York, N. Y.

a high chloride, thus presenting a false picture to the clinician, and one harmful to the patient.

3. Reporting the results to a responsible party: Telephoning laboratory reports to a ward attendant is usually tantamount to inviting a repeat test. Results of chemical examinations should be reported, preferably in writing, to the physician ordering the tests, but in the event of an "emergency" request it should be given to him or an assistant by phone.

4. Knowledge of the limitations of the methods, both chemical and clinical: These must be impressed on chemist and clinician alike. The chemist must know that fructose will not give as great a reduction as glucose in the procedure for blood sugar, and also that one need not get excited over a change in the icterus index from 120 to 85 units, as the method is hardly accurate to within 15 units in that particular range. Such knowledge may save the patient from a hasty and mistaken diagnosis.

5. Interpretation of results to the clinician and teaching of interns and residents: This requires a knowledge of the physiological, and to some extent the pathological, meaning of the results of clinical chemical procedures. Many outmoded procedures could be dropped, and newer ones properly evaluated, if clinicians and chemists discussed with each other the meanings of chemical tests, and perhaps a little of their history.

6. Training of laboratory technicians: The laboratory technicians are directly responsible for performing tests under the guidance of the clinical chemist. It is the latter's responsibility to teach the technique of performing tests, the limitations of the procedures, and the methods of calculation and reporting. Technicians should be impressed with the limits of accuracy of procedures, and they should realize that reporting a result to four (insignificant) figures does not make the tests more accurate. If a standard is good to five figures, but the photometer reading is good to only two, it is a waste of time to calculate the final answer to more than two significant figures. Care and use of instruments, which represent a substantial financial investment, must be taught the technicians.

In addition to these duties, the clinical chemist will have to choose and set up methods for use in his laboratory. The purpose of this volume is to lessen the burden of his task by providing him with a selection of tested methods suitable for use.

Collection of Blood Samples

The responsibility of the clinical chemist starts with the collection of the sample. Even if he doesn't draw the blood himself, the chemist is usually responsible for the preparation of the specimen containers, and he certainly should see that the material he receives is the proper specimen for the procedure ordered, is sufficient in quantity, and reaches the laboratory promptly.

Should the chemist be required to draw blood, there are several precautions which may aid him in collecting the specimen without violating the rules of sterility and with minimum trauma to the patient and himself.

The syringes and needles used for venipuncture should be cleaned thoroughly, then rinsed with copious amounts of distilled water. Rinsing is extremely important, especially when detergents are used. These play havoc with many tests, such as blood urea and carbon dioxide. Sterility of syringes and needles must be scrupulously maintained. They should be individually wrapped and then auto-claved for 30 minutes at 15 pounds pressure. This is the best method of assuring inactivation of the infectious hepatitis virus. Once a needle and syringe have been unwrapped, they should not be used again without resterilization.

Blood can be highly infectious, and care should be taken not to get samples onto the skin or into the mouth. If a sample is spilled on the skin or work bench, the area should be considered contaminated and washed immediately with soap and water. If blood is aspirated into the mouth, the mouth should be rinsed well with water.

Before blood is taken, the patient's arm is inspected for a suitable vein. A tourniquet is lightly applied to the upper arm. If veins are not easily palpable, it may be necessary to slap the antecubital area with the finger or to place a hot compress on the area for several minutes. This procedure usually results in the veins standing out clearly. The site of the venipuncture should be cleaned with absorbent cotton or clean gauze moistened with alcohol.

The needle should be sharp and free from burrs. If possible, the vein should be entered cleanly from above. Tissue juice may invalidate procedures such as prothrombin time. Occasionally, it will be easier to pierce the skin with a short jab, then enter the vein from the side, and thread the needle well into the lumen of the vein.

When venipuncture is successful, blood will appear in the syringe, either spontaneously or after gentle aspiration. The tourniquet is removed, and the required amount of blood is drawn into the syringe. It is probably better to use a large needle (21 or 20 gauge) when substantial quantities of blood are to be drawn, for the initial pain is often easier to bear than the annoyance of a prolonged venipuncture, and the danger of clotting is minimized. Gentle aspiration prevents foaming of the blood in the syringe.

After sufficient blood is drawn, the needle is removed from the vein, and the venipuncture site is covered with a sponge moistened with alcohol. Pressure is maintained on the sponge for 2 or 3 minutes, or the patient can elevate his arm for a short while. This will cause bleeding to stop.

The needle is taken off the syringe, and the blood is squirted gently into the proper containers. Forcing blood through a narrow needle often causes hemolysis. Containers should be labeled with the patient's name and other necessary information, such as the date and time of collection, hospital number, and type of test required. Unlabeled bottles should not be accepted in the laboratory.

Containers and Anticoagulants

Containers must be clean and dry. Those for unclotted blood must be properly prepared with the correct amounts and types of anticoagulants. The anticoagulants of choice for different procedures are given below: Lithium oxalate (or potassium or sodium oxalate)—blood alcohol, amino acids, ascorbic acid, carbon dioxide, carbon monoxide, chlorides, cholesterol, creatine, creatinine, total lipids, non-protein nitrogen, proteins, salicylates, sulfonamides, thiocynates, urea nitrogen, uric acid, (glucose). Sodium fluoride—glucose, (blood alcohol, creatinine, non-protein nitrogen). The anticoagulants are of secondary choice for those procedures enclosed in the parentheses. Sodium fluoride does have the advantage of preventing decomposition, as well as coagulation, but it interferes with enzymatic determinations.

One and one-half milligrams of lithium oxalate per milliliter of blood is recommended as anticoagulant. This is best placed in the container as an aqueous solution, which is then freed of water in an oven. After the oxalate is scraped from the sides of the bottle, the container is ready for use. Remember that some procedures require special anticoagulants.

Receipt of Material in the Laboratory

A register of all routine and "emergency" requests should be kept. Each patient's name, and the tests requested routinely, should be entered. All "emergency" requests, when registered, should be designated in a significant manner and given special care. Each patient is then assigned a number for identifying samples of his blood. When tests are completed, the results are entered opposite the patient's name. This will serve as a permanent record of the laboratory's routine and emergency requests.

After receipt and entry in the register, specimens should be sorted according to type of sample—the clotted blood tubes placed in the centrifuge for separation of the serum, the required amount of oxalated blood removed for filtrates, and the remainder of the oxalated tubes spun to separate the plasma. Processed plasma, sera, and whole blood are then distributed to the proper work benches, and the day's tests are begun.

Use and Care of Photometers

Many laboratory procedures are adaptable to photometry. If a compound is present in solution, or if one can be formed, which will absorb light over some range of the spectrum, and if that light absorption is proportional to the concentration of the compound, then photometry may be used to help determine the quantity of compound present. This fact requires only that the compound in question absorb light in a given region of the spectrum. As dirt, finger marks, and precipitates will block passage of light, they will give rise to apparent high absorption, and therefore falsely high concentrations.

Photometers are provided with filters or monochromators to delineate the wavelengths of light to be passed through the cuvettes, with photocells to detect the light transmitted, and with galvanometers to indicate the fraction of the light started through the cuvette ("incident light") which finally reaches the photo cells. There are many types of photometers on the market, but the choice of one or more for the routine clinical laboratory will depend not only on cost but also on the requirements as to sensitivity of the instrument, spectral range covered, stability (those without amplifier circuits are generally less prone to drift), ruggedness, adaptability to both micro and macro procedures, type of scale employed (conversion from per cent transmittance to optical density is time-consuming and may lead to error), necessity for special cuvettes (machines using matched test tubes are especially convenient for clinical procedures), and source of current (batteries are a nuisance, but they are also the only reliable source of current of constant voltage).

When photometers are used, it is generally best to run several standards along with the day's unknown samples. Because of day-to-day variations in individual technique, in laboratory conditions, and in the characteristics of.photometers, calibration charts should be viewed with suspicion. If used, they must be checked frequently.

The nature of light absorption is such that it does not vary linearly with molecular concentration but increases logarithmically with an increase in the number of absorbing molecules. When light absorption increases, optical density increases, and the fraction of incident light transmitted by the solution (per cent transmission) decreases. The optical density thus varies linearly with molecular concentration and may be used to aid in determining the concentration of the compound in the cuvette.

If the particular machine used has a scale calibrated in per cent transmission, it will be necessary to convert the readings to optical density. Optical density equals the logarithm of the ratio of the incident light to the transmitted light, and the incident light intensity is taken as the 100% reading on the galvanometer. Since the logarithm of 100 is 2, then 2 minus the logarithm of the reading of the sample equals the density, which is directly proportional to the color intensity. The optical density can usually be read from a conversion chart.

To calculate the fraction of the standard represented by an unknown, the ratio (optical density of unknown optical density of standard) is multiplied by the amount of standard substance used. Of course, any dilutions made, and the amount of sample used, must be taken into consideration. The final formula for calculating the concentration of an unknown in terms of 100 ml. of blood or plasma is

$$C_u = C_s \times \frac{D_u}{D_s} \times \frac{100 \text{ ml.}}{\text{Volume of the sample used}} \times \frac{V_u}{V_s}$$

where C_u = concentration of the unknown.

C_s = concentration of the standard.

D_u = optical density of the unknown.

D_s = optical density of the standard.

V_u = final volume of the unknown.

V_s = final volume of the standard.

Photometers should be treated carefully. They should be placed on a bench free from vibration. Care should be taken to avoid spilling reagents on them, or into the cuvette holders. The cuvettes should be checked before use for finger marks. The clarity of the solution should be checked, and cloudy solutions should be discarded. Cuvettes should be tested against each other before use by filling them with water, then comparing the apparent optical densities in the photometer. Cuvettes which fluctuate more than $\frac{1}{4}$ division from the mean should be discarded. If the cuvettes are round in cross section, the optical density should not vary more than $\frac{1}{2}$ galvanometer division when the cuvettes are rotated about their long axis.

An attempt has been made to describe some of the procedures which, although not necessarily chemical, are often entrusted to the care of the clinical chemist. Descriptions of these techniques are often difficult to find in laboratory texts.

To those whose methods are already more good habit than thought, perhaps this will serve as an aid in teaching students a few of their duties and some of the basic techniques of their profession, and will call to mind again several of those pitfalls of instrumentation we must all constantly guard against. The use of good technique and proven methods will assure the clinician of results on which he may base sound judgments as to diagnosis and therapy.

Amylase

Submitted by: Nelson F. Young, Department of Clinical Pathology and Hospital Laboratories, Medical College of Virginia, Richmond, Virginia.

Checked by: Margaret M. Kaser, Veterans Administration Center, Wood, Wisconsin.

Author: M. Somogyi, *Proc. Soc. Exptl. Biol. Med.* **32**: 538 (1934) (Modified).

Introduction

As is the case with nearly all enzyme activity estimations, the ability to reproduce serum amylase values depends on rigid adherence to an arbitrary set of conditions. Serum amylase activity may be demonstrated under a variety of conditions of time, temperature, substrate quality, etc. The clinical value of the estimation, however, lies solely in the comparison of activity in the suspect sample and "normal" activity as previously established under identical conditions on a series of normal individuals. It is evident, then, that the method described here cannot represent the "right" way to do amylase determinations but rather has been chosen as one of many satisfactory means of comparing the diastatic activity of unknown samples with that of normal materials.

Principle

Amylase activity is recognized through the ability of the enzyme to degrade vegetable starch and its breakdown products. During its action, reducing carbohydrates, notably maltose, are formed. This method depends on the determination of the amount of reducing sugars formed by the enzyme contained in 1 ml. of plasma or serum. The results are expressed in terms of milligrams of glucose per 100 ml. of plasma measured by the increase of reducing substances after incubation of a starch-serum mixture, above the amount in the serum alone.

8

Reagents

1. Boil 1.5 g. of Lintner soluble starch in about 70 ml. of water, cool, and make to volume of 100 ml. with $M/15$ phosphate buffer at pH 7.2. Buffer 17.9 g. $Na_2HPO_4 \cdot 12H_2O$ plus 2.3. g. KH_2PO_4 per liter.
2. 5% $CuSO_4 \cdot 5H_2O$.
3. 7% sodium tungstate $(Na_2WO_4 \cdot 2H_2O)$.
4. Reagents for sugar estimation.

Procedure

Place 1 ml. of plasma and 6 ml. of water into each of two test tubes. Place the tubes in a 40° C. water bath, and after temperature equilibration add to one of them 1 ml. of starch solution, and mix (test). After exactly 30 minutes remove the tubes from the bath. Add to each 1 ml. of $CuSO_4$ solution, and shake. Add 1 ml. of starch to the control tube. Add 1 ml. of 7% tungstate to each tube, and shake. Filter, and determine the amount of reducing sugar in the filtrate. (See Discussion.)

Calculate the reducing substance in each tube as milligrams per cent of glucose. Subtract the control tube value from the "test" value. The difference equals the reducing substance produced by amylase in 100 ml. of serum expressed as glucose.

Discussion

Since no pure homogenous substrate for amylase is available, soluble starch seems as uniform and dependable as any other. The solution recommended here is stable for at least a week in the refrigerator and is stable indefinitely if heat-sterilized. The amount of reducing sugar in it is very low, and the value obtained in the control tube closely approximates the blood sugar value. In this connection it is well to point out that high blood sugar values decrease the precision of the method, since the amylase activity is measured by difference.

1.5% cornstarch may be substituted for soluble starch if filtrates are cloudy. This may happen with some samples of soluble starch.

It must be emphasized that the sugar produced is not glucose but maltose and probably other saccharides of higher molecular weight.

For this reason the sugar method used has some influence on the results obtained. Saccharoid interference (non-sugar reducers) in the serum do not influence the results, however, since they are present in both test and control tubes.

Several modifications of the Folin-Wu method were tried in connection with the amylase procedure and found to give substantial agreement. These included the original Folin-Wu method, the second Folin modification, and the Sahyun modification. All these methods give a maltose/glucose reduction ratio of about 0.4. It seems reasonable to suppose that any sugar method which approximates this figure might be used without seriously altering the interpretation of the test.

Normal Values

One hundred consecutive blood donors were selected as subjects. Blood amylases were performed in duplicate immediately after blood was withdrawn. None of the duplicates failed to check within 8 mg. %. The distribution of the results was as follows:

40– 60 units	3
60– 80 units	17
80–100 units	32
100–120 units	29
120–140 units	12
140–160 units	6
160–180 units	1

The average value was 98 mg. % (Folin-Wu sugar Method).

Interpretation

Blood amylase is greatly increased (200–1000 units) in acute non-hemorrhagic pancreatitis early in the course of the disease. This elevation may persist for a few hours or a few days, depending on the acuteness of the attack. Chronic pancreatitis rarely gives an elevation. Hemorrhagic disease of the pancreas gives variable results. Elevations may be noted in pneumonia, thyrotoxicosis, and nephritis with azotemia. Low values may be found after the acute elevation in pancreatitis and in hepatitis and cirrhosis of the liver.

Bilirubin

Submitted by: GEORGE R. KINGSLEY, G. GETCHELL, and R. R. SCHAFFERT, Veterans Administration Center, Los Angeles, California.

Checked by: CAPT. DAVID SELIGSON and MARJORIE KNOWLTON, Department of Hepatic and Metabolic Disease, Walter Reed Army Medical Center, Washington, D. C.
ALBERT E. SOBEL, Jewish Hospital of Brooklyn, Brooklyn, New York.

Authors: H. T. MALLOY and K. A. EVELYN, *J. Biol. Chem.* **119**: 480 (1937)

Introduction

Bilirubin in serum is converted to a red-violet azobilirubin when treated with Ehrlich's reagent (diazotized sulfanilic acid). A 1-minute and a 15-minute direct-reading bilirubin are estimated in aqueous solution. More azobilirubin color is formed upon the addition of methyl alcohol, which releases protein-bound indirect bilirubin. The diazo reaction was first applied to serum bilirubin by Van den Bergh in 1918 (1): Two distinct types of reaction were noted—a "direct," or "fast," reaction, and an "indirect," or "delayed," reaction. The latter reaction was enhanced by the addition of alcohol. The term "biphasic" was applied by others (2), when both types of bilirubin reactivity were present. The delayed, or indirect, reacting bilirubin is attached to the globin of the hemoglobin molecule (3) or to plasma albumin (4). The prompt reacting type is sodium bilirubinate (5). It has been suggested that the prompt, or direct, reacting serum bilirubin be determined 1 minute after the addition of the diazo reagent to the diluted serum (6).

Reagents

1. Absolute methyl alcohol, c.p. or reagent grade.

2. Diazo reagent: SOLUTION A—Dissolve 1 g. of sulfanilic acid in 15 ml. of conc. HCl (c.p. or reagent grade), and dilute with distilled water to 1 l. (this solution is stable indefinitely). SOLUTION

11

B—Dissolve 0.5 g. of sodium nitrite (c.p. or reagent grade) in distilled water, and dilute to 100 ml. Prepare fresh before use.

3. Mixed diazo reagent: Mix 10 ml. of solution A with 0.3 ml. of solution B. (This solution must be used within 10–20 minutes after mixing.)

4. Hydrochloric acid solution for blank: Dilute 15 ml. of conc. HCl to 1 l. with distilled water.

5. Stock bilirubin standard: Dissolve 20 mg. of reagent or c.p. bilirubin in reagent grade chloroform, and dilute to 100 ml. at the temperature of cold storage (1 ml. = 0.2 mg. of bilirubin).

STANDARDIZATION: Dilute 5 ml. of stock bilirubin standard to 100 ml. with absolute methyl alcohol (1 ml. = 0.01 mg.). Dilute 0.5, 1, 2, 3, 4, and 5 ml. of this standard to 5 ml. with absolute methyl alcohol. Add 2.0 ml. of diazo reagent to 3 ml. of each of these dilutions in a standard cuvette or tube (3 ml. of 1:5 dilution = 0.006 mg.). Mix. Let stand 1 minute. Add 4.0 ml. of distilled water, and mix. Prepare a blank by adding 2 ml. of diazo reagent to 3 ml. of absolute methyl alcohol in a standard cuvette or tube. Mix. Let stand 1 minute, and add 4 ml. of distilled water. Mix. If turbidity develops in any tubes, warm to 37° C. (Increased temperature does not alter development or density of color.) Let tubes stand 10 minutes for color development. Set blank tube at 100% transmission with 560-mμ light transmission. Prepare a standard table for the calculation of total bilirubin by plotting per cent transmission against milligrams of bilirubin per 100 ml. of serum. A table may also be prepared from the average K value of the standards.

Procedure

If the icterus index is above 30, less than 1.0 ml. must be used. Use 0.5 ml. of serum if the index is 30–60, 0.2 if the index is 60–150 and 0.1 if the index is above 150. Add 2 ml. of freshly mixed diazo reagent to 1.0 ml. of fresh unhemolyzed serum (or less serum diluted to 1.0 ml.) in a standard cuvette or tube (A). At the same time add 2 ml. of dilute HCl solution to a 1.0-ml. aliquot of the serum for the preparation of a blank in a standard cuvette or tube (B). Add 3 ml. of distilled water to both tubes and mix thoroughly.

1. One-minute bilirubin: Read tube A exactly 1 minute after mixing against tube B set at 100% T with 540-mμ light transmission for the estimation of 1-minute bilirubin. Twirl tubes if necessary to remove gas bubbles from inner cuvette surfaces before making readings. Take this precaution also in reading direct and total bilirubin.

2. Direct bilirubin: Let tubes A and B continue to stand until 15 minutes have elapsed after mixing. Exactly 15 minutes after mixing, again read A against tube B, as described above.

3. Total bilirubin: Add 3 ml. of absolute methyl alcohol to tubes A and B, and quickly mix thoroughly. Read in the photometer, as described above, 10 minutes after addition of the alcohol. The color is stable for at least 30 minutes.

4. Recovery control: Add 1 ml. of serum containing 1 mg. % or less of bilirubin to each of four standard cuvettes or tubes numbered (1) standard bilirubin + serum bilirubin, (2) serum bilirubin, (3) blank for standard bilirubin + serum bilirubin, and (4) blank for serum bilirubin. Add 2 ml. of freshly prepared diazo reagent to tubes 1 and 2. Add 2 ml. of dilute HCl solution to tubes 3 and 4. Add 3 ml. of distilled water to all four tubes, and mix thoroughly. Let stand 15 minutes. Add 1 ml. of dilute stock bilirubin standard (0.01 mg.) and 2 ml. of absolute methyl alcohol to tubes 1 and 3, and quickly mix thoroughly. Read tube 1 exactly 10 minutes after mixing with alcohol against tube 3 set at 100% transmission with 540-mμ light transmission for the estimation of standard bilirubin + serum bilirubin. Add 3 ml. of absolute methyl alcohol to tubes 2 and 4 and quickly mix thoroughly. After 10 minutes read tube 2 against tube 4 in the same manner as for the estimation of serum bilirubin.

Incubate tubes at 37° C. if necessary to prevent turbidity.

Per cent recovery =

$$\frac{[(\text{Standard bilirubin}^* + \text{serum bilirubin})^* - \text{serum bilirubin}]^*}{1} \times 100$$

* Mg. per 100 ml.

Calculation

One-minute bilirubin: Mg. per 100 ml. = $\frac{2}{3}K^*(2 - \log\%T)$.
Direct bilirubin: Mg. per 100 ml. = $\frac{2}{3}K^*(2 - \log\%T)$.
Total bilirubin: Mg. per 100 ml. = $K^*(2 - \log\%T)$.
Indirect bilirubin: Total bilirubin − direct bilirubin.

* K = 7.0 Coleman spectrophotometer No. 14, cuvette 6–304B.

Normal Values

One-minute bilirubin: 0.06–0.25 mg. %.
Total bilirubin: 0.3–1.5 mg. %.
Indirect bilirubin: 0.06–0.8 mg. %.

The normal range of the bilirubin fractions obtained by this method agrees essentially with that reported in an extensive study (7), in which a modification of the method of Malloy and Evelyn (8) was used. This study indicated that "the mean normal 1 minute bilirubin is 0.11 ± 0.05 mg. %. The mean total bilirubin is 0.62 ± 0.25 mg. %. The upper limit of normal for the 1 minute determination is 0.25 mg. %; for the total determination, 1.5 mg. %."

Abnormal Values

A study (7) of thirty-two abnormal subjects gave a range of 0.24–24.95 mg. % of 1-minute bilirubin and a range of 1.6–44.5 mg. % of total bilirubin. The ratio of prompt reacting or 1-minute bilirubin to total bilirubin is elevated in those diseases or phases of diseases wherein obstruction to the pigment outflow tract of the liver occurs, e.g., carcinoma of head of pancreas, tumor of bile duct, calculosis of common duct or hepatic duct, certain phases of cirrhosis, and cholangeolytic form of hepatitis, etc. It is lowered in hemolytic processes resulting in jaundice and acquired hemolytic jaundice, etc.

Comments

Results by this proposed method give results similar to those of the Watson-Ducci method. Even though the latter method uses larger dilutions, the per cent transmittance as determined in both methods is about the same.

It should be noted that, when serum is diluted, the estimated bilirubin content increases per unit of serum.

The importance of the 15-minute bilirubin is of doubtful clinical value.

Serial determinations on unchanging cases show surprising reproductibility of the 1-minute and total serum bilirubin, even though many of these measurements are made at the suboptimal part of the colorimeter scale. It is believed that this method is reliable to 10% or better on individual analyses.

It is reported by Zieve *et al.* (7) that the upper limit of normal serum bilirubin, 1-minute, and total, is 0.25 and 1.50 mg. %, respectively. These values are found in 1% of the population. Since viral hepatitis and other liver diseases are not uncommon, it is difficult to state that high values such as 1.50 mg. % are normal.

Precautions and Notes

1. Serum must be fresh and unhemolyzed. Bilirubin on standing may be altered by light, by chemical action, and by enzymes. Serum is preferable to plasma.

2. Sodium nitrite and diazo reagent must be pure and freshly prepared.

3. In the method presented, standards containing more than 0.03 mg. of bilirubin fail to obey Beer's law, and for that reason serum specimens containing more than 3 mg. % of bilirubin should be diluted to a concentration within this range.

4. It is best to use 540-mμ light transmission, since bilirubin present in serum and pure bilirubin added to serum has a maximum absorption at this wavelength of light. Pure bilirubin standards have a maximum absorption at 560 mμ.

5. Diazo reagent must be added to the standards before the addition of distilled water for dilution; otherwise full color development may not take place.

6. Control standards of 0.01 and 0.03 mg. bilirubin and a recovery control should be run frequently as a check on the constancy of the standardization.

BIBLIOGRAPHY

1. Van den Bergh, H., *Gallenfarbstoff im Blute*, Van Doesburgh, S. C., Leiden, 1st ed., 1918.
2. Feigl, J., and Querner, E., *Z. ges. exptl. Med.* **9**: 153 (1919).
3. Watson, C. J., *Blood* **1**: 99 (1946).
4. Coolidge, T. B., *J. Biol. Chem.* **132**: 119 (1940).
5. Hunter, G., *Brit. J. Exptl. Pathol.* **11**: 415 (1930).
6. Ducci, H., and Watson, C. J., *J. Lab. Clin. Med.* **30**: 293 (1945).
7. Zieve, L., Hill, E., Hanson, M., Falcone, A. B., and Watson, C. J., *J. Lab. Clin. Med.* **38**: 446 (1951).
8. Malloy, H. T., and Evelyn, K. A., *J. Biol. Chem.* **119**: 480 (1937).

Calcium

Submitted by: OTTO SCHALES, Alton Ochsner Medical Foundation, New Orleans, Louisiana.

Checked by: MIRIAM REINER, Gallinger Municipal Hospital, Washington, D. C.

Authors: B. KRAMER and F. F. TISDALL, *J. Biol. Chem.* **47:** 475 (1921).
E. P. CLARK and J. B. COLLIP, *J. Biol. Chem.* **63:** 461 (1925).

Introduction

The calcium of the blood serum is precipitated as calcium oxalate which is washed with ammonium hydroxide. The precipitate is dissolved in dilute sulfuric acid and titrated while hot with permanganate to the same end point used in the standardization of the permanganate solution.

Reagents

1. Saturated ammonium oxalate solution: Add about 20 g. of ammonium oxalate to 100 ml. of water, shake repeatedly, and let settle overnight.

2. Ammonia water: Make by diluting 2 ml. of concentrated NH₄OH with water to 100 ml.

3. Approximately 1/N H_2SO_4: Take 2.8 ml. of concentrated sulfuric acid into a 100-ml. volumetric flask which contains about 40 or 50 ml. of water, mix, and fill to the mark with water.

4. Preparation and standardization of 0.1 N potassium permanganate solution:

(a) POTASSIUM PERMANGANATE SOLUTION: Dissolve 3.16 g. of $KMnO_4$ in 1 l. of water. Store in a glass-stoppered brown bottle for at least 1 week.

(b) OXALIC ACID SOLUTION: Grind oxalic acid ($H_2C_2O_4 \cdot 2H_2O$) to a fine powder and expose to air in the dark on a watch glass for about 2 hours with occasional stirring. Weigh out 6.3035 g., and dilute in a volumetric flask to 1 l. This is a 0.1 N solution.

(c) STANDARDIZATION OF PERMANGANATE SOLUTION: Pipette exactly 10.0 ml. of 0.1 N oxalic acid into a 250-ml. Erlenmeyer flask, add 7.5 ml. of sulfuric acid 1:5 (10 ml. of concentrated H_2SO_4 added to 40 ml. of water) and about 100 ml. of water heated to 80° C. Titrate the hot mixture with $KMnO_4$ solution from a 25-ml. burette to the first pink color, which persists for 30 seconds. Average the result of three titrations. The normality of the permanganate solution is in this case the reciprocal of the number of milliliters used.

5. 0.005 N permanganate solution: Measure the exact amount of 0.1 N $KMnO_4$ which was necessary to oxidize 10.0 ml. of 0.1 N oxalic acid into a 200-ml. volumetric flask, and fill to the mark with water. The 0.005 N permanganate solution is unstable and has to be used within 1 hour.

Procedure

Mix 2 ml. of serum with 2 ml. of water in a 15-ml. pointed centrifuge tube. Add 1 ml. of saturated ammonium oxalate solution, mix, and let stand for at least half an hour. Then centrifuge the tube at about 2000 r.p.m. (International centrifuge, size 1) for 10 minutes. Decant the supernatant fluid, and wipe the mouth of the tube dry, invert it, and drain it on filter paper for at least 5 minutes. Dry the mouth again, and wash the precipitate by blowing 4 ml. of ammonia water on it. Use some of this ammonia water to rinse the wall of the centrifuge tube. Do not allow the tube to stand around after the addition of ammonia water because calcium oxalate is slightly soluble in it. Centrifuge, and drain as before. Add 2 ml. of N sulfuric acid, and heat in boiling water, until all precipitate is dissolved. Titrate the liberated oxalic acid, while hot, with 0.005 N permanganate to a first faint pink color, which persists for about 30 seconds. Titrate a blank of 2 ml. of sulfuric acid to the same end point. Use a 3-ml. microburette, and read to the nearest 0.01 ml. A normal serum calcium requires about 2 ml. of permanganate in this procedure, and a blank requires about 0.02 ml., depending on the sulfuric acid.

Calculation

1. 1 ml. 0.005 N $KMnO_4$ = 0.1 mg. calcium.
2. (Ml. $KMnO_4$ used for unknown − ml. $KMnO_4$ used for blank) × 5 = Mg. calcium per 100 ml. serum.
3. (Ml. $KMnO_4$ used for unknown − ml. $KMnO_4$ used for blank) × 2.5 = Meq. calcium per liter serum.

Normal Values

Normal values are 4.5–5.5 meq. of calcium per liter of serum (9–11 mg. per 100 ml.).

Calcium values in children may be slightly higher than in adults. During the late months of pregnancy there may be a slight drop in calcium. Low values may be obtained in cases of hypoparathyroidism, severe nephritis, uremia, and infantile tetany.

Elevated values may be observed in cases of hyperparathyroidism and after fractures.

Carbon Dioxide Content (Titrimetric)

Submitted by: LT. M. E. HODES, Department of Physiological Chemistry, U. S. Naval Medical School, National Naval Medical Center, Bethesda, Maryland.

Checked by: MIRIAM REINER, Gallinger Municipal Hospital, Washington, D. C.

Authors: D. D. VAN SLYKE, E. STILLMAN, AND G. E. CULLEN, *J. Biol. Chem.* **38:** 167 (1919).
D. D. VAN SLYKE, *J. Biol. Chem.* **52:** 495 (1922).
T. JOHNSSON, *Acta Paediat.* **37:** 1 (1949).

Principle

A known amount of hydrochloric acid is added to serum or plasma. The solution is shaken to remove the carbon dioxide gas formed, and the excess hydrogen ion is titrated with standard base. The concentration of bicarbonate is calculated from the amount of hydrogen ion consumed in the original reaction

(1) $HCO_3^- + H^+ \rightarrow H_2CO_3 \rightarrow CO_2 + H_2O$
(2) $H^+ + OH^- \rightarrow H_2O$
$[H^+] \approx [OH^-] \approx [HCO_3^-]$

Reagents

1. Hydrochloric acid, 0.100 N stock solution: Prepare this from constant-boiling hydrochloric acid, by dilution with fresh distilled water. It is stable indefinitely and should be stored in glass or plastic air-tight containers. This is the primary standard and must be made accurately.

2. Hydrochloric acid, 0.010 N working solution: Dilute 10.0 ml. of the 0.1 N HCl to 100 ml. with CO_2-free 1% saline. This solution should be kept stoppered when not actually in use. It must be prepared fresh daily.

3. Sodium hydroxide, saturated stock solution: Prepare a liter of saturated solution of sodium hydroxide in distilled water. Allow the carbonates to settle, and use the supernatant for preparation

19

of the 0.1 N stock solution.   Store in a plastic bottle with a tightly fitting rubber stopper.

4. Sodium hydroxide, 0.100 N stock solution: Dilute about 2.7 ml. of the saturated solution of NaOH to 500 ml., using CO_2-free water.   Store this solution in a tightly stoppered plastic bottle. Prepare fresh weekly.   Standardize by titration against 4 ml. of the 0.1 N HCl, using phenol red indicator.   Adjust to exactly 0.100 N.

5. Sodium hydroxide, 0.010 N working solution: Dilute 10 ml. of the 0.100 N stock solution of NaOH to 100 ml. with CO_2-free 1% saline.   Check the titer against the 0.010 N HCl, using phenol red indicator.   Prepare fresh daily.   Keep stoppered when not in use.

6. Carbon dioxide-free water: Boil 3 l. of freshly distilled water in a 4-l. Erlenmeyer flask.   While the water is still boiling, remove the flask from the hot plate and insert a rubber stopper connected to a 500-ml. sidearm Erlenmeyer, which is in turn connected to a soda-lime tube.   Immerse the sidearm flask in an ice-salt mixture. When the water has cooled, transfer it to a tightly stoppered plastic bottle.

7. Saline, 1%: Dissolve about 20 g. of sodium chloride in 2 l. of CO_2-free water.   Keep the container tightly closed.   This solution is stable indefinitely, if kept protected from CO_2.   It may be dispensed via a burette attached directly to the bottle.

8. Phenol red indicator: Grind 0.1 g. of phenol red (phenolsulfonphthalein) in an agate mortar with 5.7 ml. of 0.05 N NaOH. Transfer to a 100-ml. volumetric flask, and dilute to volume with CO_2-free water.   Stable indefinitely.

9. Antifoam A (Dow Corning Corp.).

Procedure

1. Collection of the sample: For ordinary clinical purposes, venous blood collected without stasis is satisfactory.   Use either oxalated or clotted blood.   Stopper the sample after collection, and run the test as soon as possible.   Separate the plasma or serum from the cells, and store in a stoppered tube.

2. Titration of the sample: Touch the end of a stirring rod to some Antifoam A.   Rotate the stirring rod in the tube of plasma.

PREPARATION OF THE STANDARD: Place 6 ml. of 1% saline in a 25-ml. Erlenmeyer flask.   Add 0.10 ml. of serum or plasma from a

Mohr pipette. Add 2 drops of phenol red indicator. Insert a rubber stopper, and rotate gently to mix the contents.

TITRATION OF SAMPLE (always run in duplicate when 0.1-ml. sample is used):

Place 0.1 ml. of serum or plasma in a 25-ml. Erlenmeyer flask, and then add 1.00 ml. of 0.01 N HCl and 4 ml. of 1% saline. Swirl the flask vigorously for at least 1 minute to allow the CO_2 to escape.

Add 2 drops of phenol red indicator and then add 0.01 N NaOH dropwise, but rapidly, from a pipette until a pink color matching the standard has persisted for at least 15 seconds. Record the pipette reading. Note: Toward the end point, the color tends to turn, then fade, after each drop is added.

Calculation

1. 1.00 − ml. NaOH used in the back titration = Ml. 0.010 N HCl equivalent to HCO_3^- present in serum or plasma.

2. (a) Ml. 0.010 N HCl × 100 = Milliequivalents per liter (meq./l.) HCO_3^-.

   (b) Ml. 0.010 N HCl × 222.6 = HCO_3^- content in volumes per 100 ml.

3. A chart may be prepared relating the milliliters of NaOH used in back titration to the HCO_3^- content.

Comments

This test actually determines the bicarbonate concentration of serum or plasma, rather than the total carbon dioxide content. The difference is about +3 vol. % (1.3 meq./l.) for normal blood, as a result of the failure of the present method to determine the carbon dioxide dissolved in plasma.

For the complete evaluation of the state of acid-base balance of a patient according to the Henderson-Hasselbalch equation, one other fact must be known—either the total CO_2 content, the pH, or the dissolved CO_2 content or partial pressure.

$$pH = 6.1 + \log \frac{[HCO_3^-]}{[H_2CO_3]} = 6.1 + \log \frac{[HCO_3^-]}{[\text{dissolved } CO_2]}$$

However, for most clinical work, the bicarbonate concentration alone can be used as a diagnostic aid. When the concentration of HCO_3^- is increased, the most common cause is metabolic alkalosis, though (partly) compensated respiratory acidosis may be at fault. When the HCO_3^- concentration is lowered, the usual reason behind this observation is metabolic acidosis, though (partly) compensated respiratory alkalosis may be the cause.

The normal HCO_3^- concentration of plasma or serum is about 25 meq./l. (55.7 vol. %), with a range of from about 21 meq./l. (46.7 vol. %) to 30 meq./l. (66.8 vol. %). Values in children may range about 4.5 meq./l. (10 vol. %) lower.

Since the dissolved CO_2 is not determined by this procedure, it cannot be used for the determination of the CO_2 combining power, as the dissolved CO_2 must be adjusted to a level consonant with the partial pressure of CO_2 present in the alveoli of the operator.

This test may be performed on a macro scale, using 5.0 ml. of acid and 1.0 ml. of serum or plasma in the standard and in the titration, or on a semimicro scale, using 2.5 ml. of acid and 0.5 ml. of serum. In the latter case the final answer must be multiplied by 2.

Carbon Dioxide Determination by the Van Slyke Volumetric and Manometric Apparatus

Submitted by: MIRIAM REINER, Gallinger Municipal Hospital, Washington, D. C.

Checked by: JULIUS J. CARR, The Mount Sinai Hospital, New York, New York.

Authors: D. D. VAN SLYKE and G. E. CULLEN. *J. Biol. Chem.* **19:** 211 (1914).
D. D. VAN SLYKE and W. C. STADIE, *J. Biol. Chem.* **49:** 1 (1921).
D. D. VAN SLYKE and J. M. NEILL, *J. Biol. Chem.* **61:** 523 (1924).

Introduction

The plasma from well-oxalated blood is shaken in a separatory funnel from which the air is displaced either by alveolar air from the lungs of the operator or by a 5.5% carbon dioxide-air mixture, so that the blood combines with as much carbon dioxide as it can hold under normal tension. The saturated plasma is measured and acidified in the Van Slyke volumetric gas apparatus, and the liberated carbon dioxide is measured and calculated, taking into account temperature and atmospheric conditions.

The volumetric apparatus consists essentially of a 50-ml. pipette with a cock sealed at each end, the lower end being attached to a heavy-walled bulb, the upper end serving as a receptacle for blood samples and reagents. The stem of the pipette at the upper end is calibrated in 0.02-ml. marks for a space of 1 ml. for the measurement of gases.

The analysis is carried out by filling the apparatus with mercury and putting in the blood samples preceded by, or followed by, reagents to free the gases. The gases are extracted from the solution by lowering the mercury until a vacuum is obtained in the pipette, which is shaken for 1–3 minutes. The liquid is then drawn off into a small bulb sealed on the bottom, and the mercury is re-admitted until pressure is restored to atmospheric. The volume of gas is read in the graduated upper stem of the pipette. When a mixture of gases is obtained, carbon dioxide is absorbed with alkali,

23

oxygen with hydrosulfite ($Na_2S_2O_4$), and carbon monoxide with cuprous chloride solution.

Reagents

1. 1 N lactic acid (approximately): Dilute 1 vol. of concentrated lactic acid, sp. gr. 1.20, with 9 vols. of water.

2. 0.1 N lactic acid (approximately): Dilute normal lactic acid (reagent 1) with 9 vol. of water. Deaerate or boil to remove carbon dioxide.

3. 18 N (saturated) CO_2-free sodium hydroxide: Dissolve NaOH in an equal weight of water. Let the solution stand in a paraffin-lined or polyethylene bottle until the carbonate has settled.

4. 5 N NaOH, 20%: Take 27 ml. of reagent 3, diluted to 100 ml. Protect it from atmospheric CO_2 with a soda-lime tube.

5. N NaOH (approximately): Dilute 1 vol. of reagent 4 with 4 vol. of CO_2-free water.

6. Caprylic alcohol.

Test for Leakage

Test for leaks before beginning a series of analyses in either volumetric or manometric apparatus. Introduce 2 or 3 ml. of water into the chamber, and extract the air by shaking. Read the volume of extracted gas, and repeat the extraction. An increase in volume or pressure indicates leakage of air into the evacuated apparatus.

The cause of the leak is usually improper grinding or lubrication of the upper stopcock, or possibly diffusion of air through the rubber connecting the chamber with the leveling bulb. "Nitrometer" tubing of heavy-walled, greyish red rubber seems to be the least porous, but even that deteriorates after months of use. In the volumetric apparatus, keep the leveling bulb routinely in position 2.

All stopcocks must be well ground and lubricated so that they turn smoothly and do not leak. Stopcocks and connections must be scrupulously clean before lubrication. First apply a thin layer of vaseline to the core of the stopcock, then a thin layer of vaseline-rubber-paraffin lubricant. Remove any lubricant that enters the bore of the stopcock and adjoining connections. Use only minimal amount of grease in a ring at each end of the stopcock, and work it in by turning the core in its casing. A well-lubricated cock should appear transparent throughout and should turn with perfect ease.

Measurement of Samples

For delivery of 1–2-ml. samples of blood, pipettes with heavy-walled capillary stems of 1-mm. bore and provided with stopcocks are most satisfactory. They are calibrated to deliver between two marks, one on the upper stem and one above the cock on the lower stem. A tapered rubber tip is provided so that the pipette will fit into the bottom of the cup above the gas chamber.

For delivery of samples of 0.5 ml. or less, pipettes calibrated for blowing out delivery are generally used. Rest the pipette tip on the bottom of the cup which is partially filled with water or reagent. As blood flows out from the tip of the pipette, open the cock at the top of the chamber enough so that fluid flows into the chamber a little faster than blood flows out of the pipette. The blood therefore flows continuously into the chamber with a stream of water or reagent solution from the cup.

After adding any absorbent solution through the upper cock, run a little mercury through the cock to prevent the liquid from adhering to the underside of the cock. Always allow 1 minute after adding absorbent solution for it to drain completely down the walls before measuring the gas volume. Always read the bottom of the water meniscus in the chamber.

Keep the curved capillary outlet at the left of the cock of the chamber continually filled with mercury. The other bore leading to the cup must be filled with mercury each time before the chamber is evacuated. To prevent trapping of air when sealing with mercury, fill the cup halfway with water, and then drop in 0.2 ml. of mercury. Admit the mercury into the chamber until just enough is left above the cock to fill the capillary leading up to the cup. After the cock is sealed, remove the water from the cup and continue the analysis.

CARBON DIOXIDE CAPACITY OF PLASMA (ALKALI RESERVE), VOLUMETRIC APPARATUS

Procedure

Transfer 3 ml. of plasma (centrifuged under oil) to a 300-ml. separatory funnel connected with a bottle containing glass beads. The air within the funnel is displaced by alveolar air from the lungs of the operator, who, after inspiring normally, expires as quickly and completely as possible through the glass beads and separatory funnel. A 5.5% CO_2–air mixture from a tank and passed over glass beads may be used also. Insert the stopper of the funnel just before expiration is finished, so that air will not be drawn back into the funnel. To saturate the plasma, rotate the funnel on its axis for 2 minutes, distributing the plasma in a thin layer over the surface. After saturation is complete, place the funnel upright, and allow it to stand for a few minutes until the fluid has drained from the walls. Fill both capillaries above the upper cock with mercury (Fig. 1).

Place one drop of caprylic alcohol in the bottom of the cup (b), and let it flow into and fill the capillary beneath. The mercury bulb should be in position 2, and the lower cock open. Place 2 ml. of 0.1 N lactic acid in the cup. Place 1 ml. of blood or plasma in the pipette in the cup, and run it into the chamber underneath the acid layer (see Fig. 2). Admit sufficient acid after the sample to bring the volume of the solution in the apparatus to 2.5 ml. Place a drop of mercury in the cup, filling the capillary and the bore of the cock (e) to act as a seal. Close the cock. Lower the mercury bulb to position 3 to extract CO_2 from the solution. Keep this position until the mercury meniscus in the chamber has fallen to the 50-ml. mark. Close the lower cock.

Return the mercury bulb to position 2. Extract CO_2 from the solution by removing the chamber from the holder and inverting it 15 or more times. It may also be attached to a motor for shaking. With whole blood rotate the solution about the walls of the chamber to avoid foam. Return the chamber to its holder, and allow it to stand for a minute to drain the fluid from the walls to the bottom. Lower the leveling bulb once more to position 3, opening the lower cock to connect the chamber with the trap (d) under the lower cock. Drain the fluid from the chamber down into the trap, being careful that no gas follows. Raise the leveling bulb as in Fig. 3. Turn the lower cock so that mercury is admitted to the chamber through the tube (c) until gas is brought to atmospheric pressure, as shown in Fig. 3. Open the stopcock gradually so that the mercury does not rise suddenly. During admission of the last part of mercury, retard the flow by partially closing the lower cock, so that the meniscus in the calibrated stem comes slowly and smoothly into the position of equilibrium with atmospheric pressure. Close the lower cock, and note the gas volume. When plasma is used,

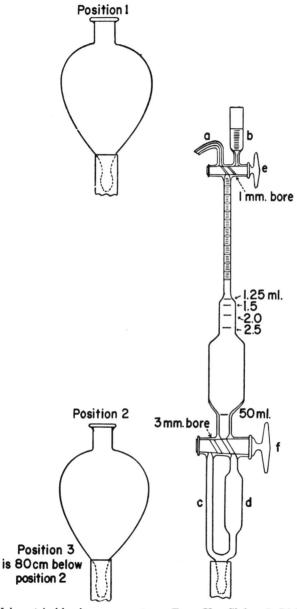

FIG. 1. Volumetric blood gas apparatus. From Van Slyke, *J. Biol. Chem.* **30**: 347 (1917).

the reading of the total gas volume may be taken as the finish of the determination. When plasma CO_2 is determined without in-

Fig. 2. Delivery of blood sample into chamber of apparatus from rubber tipped stopcock pipette. From Van Slyke and Neill, *J. Biol. Chem.* **61**: 523 (1924).

troduction of alkali, it is not necessary to wash the apparatus between analyses. When whole blood is analyzed, so much oxygen is mixed with CO_2 that it is necessary to absorb the CO_2 with alkali.

In this case extract gases, and measure the volume as in the above procedure. Lower the leveling bulb so that partial vacuum is obtained and the gas space in chamber is about 5 ml. Close the lower cock, and place 2 ml. of gas-free 1 N NaOH in the cup of the apparatus. Allow 1 ml. of NaOH to flow slowly into the chamber, taking at least 30 seconds. After alkali is admitted, seal the upper cock with mercury, allowing a few drops to flow through the stop-

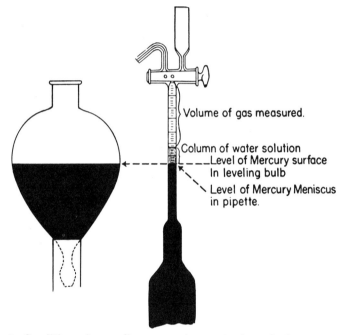

Volume of gas measured.

Column of water solution
Level of Mercury surface
In leveling bulb

Level of Mercury Meniscus
in pipette.

FIG. 3. Conditions for reading gas volume at atmospheric pressure in the volumetric blood gas apparatus. From Van Slyke, *J. Biol. Chem.* **30:** 347 (1917).

cock. Lower the leveling bulb to position 3. Draw the alkali solution into the 15-ml. bulb with other solutions. Measure the volume of unabsorbed oxygen and nitrogen. The difference between this and the first reading represents the volume of carbon dioxide.

Calculation

Calculate the *carbon dioxide content* from the factors in Table I. When the carbon dioxide volume is determined by absorption with NaOH, multiply directly by the factor indicated.

TABLE I

FACTORS FOR CALCULATING CO_2 CONTENT DETERMINED BY VOLUMETRIC APPARATUS WITH BLOOD OR PLASMA SAMPLES OF 1 ML.
(From Van Slyke and Stadie, *J. Biol. Chem.* **49**: 1 (1921))

Temperature, °C.	Air in extracted gases from plasma and water (Subtract from observed air + CO_2 volume if CO_2 and air are measured together), ml.	Factors by which milliliters of CO_2 extracted from 1 ml. plasma or blood are multiplied to give	
		CO_2, vol. %	CO_2 mM./l.
15	0.048	$100.2 \times \dfrac{B}{760}$	$44.9 \quad \dfrac{B}{760}$
16	48	99.5 "	44.7 "
17	48	98.9 "	44.4 "
18	47	98.3 "	44.2 "
19	47	97.8 "	43.9 "
20	46	97.2 "	43.7 "
21	46	96.6 "	43.4 "
22	45	96.0 "	43.1 "
23	45	95.4 "	42.9 "
24	45	94.8 "	42.6 "
25	44	94.2 "	43.3 "
26	44	93.6 "	42.1 "
27	44	93.1 "	41.8 "
28	43	92.4 "	41.5 "
29	43	91.8 "	41.3 "
30	43	91.2 "	41.0 "
31	43	90.6 "	40.7 "
32	42	90.0 "	40.4 "
33	42	89.4 "	40.2 "
34	42	88.8 "	39.9 "
Barometer	$\dfrac{\text{Barometer}}{760}$	Barometer	$\dfrac{\text{Barometer}}{760}$
732	0.961	756	0.995
734	0.996	758	0.997
736	0.967	760	1.000
738	0.971	762	1.003
740	0.974	764	1.006
742	0.976	766	1.008
744	0.979	768	1.011
746	0.981	770	1.013
748	0.984	772	1.016
750	0.987	774	1.018
752	0.989	776	1.021
754	0.992	778	1.024

When only one reading is made, as in plasma analyses, that of total carbon dioxide plus air, the estimated cubic millimeters of air held in solution under room conditions by 1.5 ml. of water plus 1 ml. of plasma (second column of Table I) is subtracted from the observed gas volume, and the remainder is multiplied by the carbon dioxide factor (third or fourth column of Table I) corresponding to the observed temperature.

In case the volume of plasma taken for the estimation of carbon dioxide content was 0.5 ml., multiply the observed volume of gas by 2 before calculating the volume per cent of bound carbon dioxide.

For the *carbon dioxide combining capacity* of blood plasma, consult Table II.

Van Slyke Manometric Gas Apparatus

The manometric gas apparatus resembles the volumetric apparatus, but the gas is compressed to an arbitrarily chosen volume and determined from the pressure exerted on a manometer, instead of from an estimation of its volume at atmospheric pressure.

In the manometric apparatus, the extracted gases are reduced to a volume a of 0.5 or 2.0 ml. (Fig. 4), and a reading P_1 is made on the manometer. The gas to be determined is then removed or absorbed, and the reading P_2 is taken with the unabsorbed gas at the same a milliliters volume. The pressure fall, $P_1 - P_2$ millimeters of mercury, between the two readings is the pressure which the determined gas exerted at a cubic milliliter volume. The volume which the gas would occupy at 0° C., 760 mm., is calculated by multiplying this pressure fall by a single factor which is a function of the temperature.

Besides the blood gases, the apparatus may be used for microdeterminations of organic nitrogen and carbon, urea, amino nitrogen, iodates, sulfates, total base, sugar, calcium, lactic acid, and nitrites, and for analyses of gas mixtures.

For very small amounts of gas, measurements of the pressure at 0.5 ml. volume is desirable. At this volume 0.01 ml. of gas exerts about 16 mm. pressure.

General Technique for Manometric Apparatus

Never lower the leveling bulb below the lower ring when the cock at the top of the extraction chamber is open to the air. If this

TABLE II

CALCULATION OF THE CARBON DIOXIDE COMBINING CAPACITY OF BLOOD PLASMA

(From Van Slyke and Cullen, *J. Biol. Chem.* **19**: 211 (1914))

Observed vol. gas × $\frac{B}{760}$	Milliliters of CO_2 reduced to 0°, 760 mm., bound as bicarbonate by 100 ml. of plasma				Observed vol. gas × $\frac{B}{760}$	Milliliters of CO_2 reduced to 0°, 760 mm., bound as bicarbonate by 100 ml. of plasma			
	15°	20°	25°	30°		15°	20°	25°	30°
0.20	9.1	9.9	10.7	11.8	0.60	47.7	48.1	48.5	48.6
1	10.1	10.9	11.7	12.6	1	48.7	49.0	49.4	49.5
2	11.0	11.8	12.6	13.5	2	49.7	50.0	50.4	50.4
3	12.0	12.8	13.6	14.3	3	50.7	51.0	51.3	51.4
4	13.0	13.7	14.5	15.2	4	51.6	51.9	52.2	52.3
5	13.9	14.7	15.5	16.1	5	52.6	52.8	53.2	53.2
6	14.9	15.7	16.4	17.0	6	53.6	53.8	54.1	54.1
7	15.9	16.6	17.4	18.0	7	54.5	54.8	55.1	55.1
8	16.8	17.6	18.3	18.9	8	55.5	55.7	56.0	56.0
9	17.8	18.5	19.2	19.8	9	56.5	56.7	57.0	56.9
0.30	18.8	19.5	20.2	20.8	0.70	57.4	57.6	57.9	57.9
1	19.7	20.4	21.1	21.7	1	58.4	58.6	58.9	58.8
2	20.7	21.4	22.1	22.6	2	59.4	59.5	59.8	59.7
3	21.7	22.3	23.0	23.5	3	60.3	60.5	60.7	60.6
4	22.6	23.3	24.0	24.5	4	61.3	61.4	61.7	61.6
5	23.6	24.2	24.9	25.4	5	62.3	62.4	62.6	62.5
6	24.6	25.2	25.8	26.3	6	63.2	63.3	63.6	63.4
7	25.5	26.2	26.8	27.3	7	64.2	64.3	64.5	64.3
8	26.5	27.1	27.7	28.2	8	65.2	65.3	65.5	65.3
9	27.5	28.1	28.7	29.1	9	66.1	66.2	66.4	66.2
0.40	28.4	29.0	29.6	30.0	0.80	67.1	67.2	67.3	67.1
1	29.4	30.0	30.5	31.0	1	68.1	68.1	68.3	68.0
2	30.3	30.9	31.5	31.9	2	69.0	69.1	69.2	69.0
3	31.3	31.9	32.4	32.8	3	70.0	70.0	70.2	69.9
4	32.3	32.8	33.4	33.8	4	71.0	71.0	71.1	70.8
5	33.2	33.8	34.3	34.7	5	71.9	72.0	72.1	71.8
6	34.2	34.7	35.3	35.6	6	72.9	72.9	73.0	72.7
7	35.2	35.7	36.2	36.5	7	73.9	73.9	74.0	73.6
8	36.1	36.6	37.2	37.4	8	74.8	74.8	74.9	74.5
9	37.1	37.6	38.1	38.4	9	75.8	75.8	75.8	75.4
0.50	38.1	38.5	39.0	39.3	0.90	76.8	76.7	76.8	76.4
1	39.1	39.5	40.0	40.3	1	77.8	77.7	77.7	77.3
2	40.0	40.4	40.9	41.2	2	78.7	78.6	78.7	78.2
3	41.0	41.4	41.9	42.1	3	79.7	79.6	79.6	79.2
4	42.0	42.4	42.8	43.0	4	80.7	80.5	80.6	80.1
5	42.9	43.3	43.8	43.9	5	81.6	81.5	81.5	81.0
6	43.9	44.3	44.7	44.9	6	82.6	82.5	82.4	82.0
7	44.9	45.3	45.7	45.8	7	83.6	83.4	83.4	82.9
8	45.8	46.2	46.6	46.7	8	84.5	84.4	84.3	83.8
9	46.8	47.1	47.5	47.6	9	85.5	85.3	85.2	84.8
0.60	47.7	48.1	48.5	48.6	1.00	86.5	86.2	86.2	85.7

happens, all the mercury in the chamber will flow into the leveling
bulb, and the air or solution will be drawn over into the manometer;
then the apparatus must be cleaned.

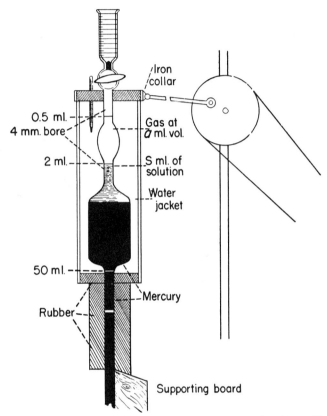

FIG. 4. Extraction chamber of manometric apparatus, showing rubber joint at
bottom and attachment of Stadie shaker at top. Gas is shown at 2 ml. volume for
pressure reading. The glass stem at the bottom of the chamber must be visible for
about 10 mm. below the 50-ml. mark. From Van Slyke and Neill, *J. Biol. Chem.*
61: 523 (1924).

To clean the manometer, open the cock at the top, draw the
mercury as completely as possible into the leveling bulb, and dis-
connect the rubber tubing. Attach the tube leading to the suction
flask where the leveling bulb was attached. Draw water through
the manometer at the open top and, if the tube is greasy, alcoholic
KOH, then acetone. Instead of KOH, cleaning solution, water,

and acetone, or nitric acid, water, and acetone may be used. When the manometer is refilled with mercury, lower the leveling bulb several times to collect any air, and expel the air bubble through the cock at the top.

TABLE III

FACTOR FOR CALCULATION OF CO_2 CONTENT OF BLOOD

(From Van Slyke and Sendroy, *J. Biol. Chem.* **73**: 127 (1927))

	Factors by which millimeter P_{CO_2} are multiplied to give:									
	CO_2, mM./l. blood					CO_2 per blood, vol. %				
Temperature, °C.	Sample = 0.2 ml.	Sample = 1.0 ml.				Sample = 0.2 ml.	Sample = 1.0 ml.			
		$S = 3.5$ ml.		$S = 7.0$ ml.			$S = 3.5$ ml.		$S = 7.0$ ml.	
	$S = 2.0$ ml. $a = 0.5$ ml. $i = 1.037$	$a = 0.5$ ml. $i = 1.037$	$a = 2.0$ ml. $i = 1.017$	$a = 0.5$ ml. $i = 1.037$	$a = 2.0$ ml. $i = 1.017$	$S = 2.0$ ml. $a = 0.5$ ml. $i = 1.037$	$a = 0.5$ ml. $i = 1.037$	$a = 2.0$ ml. $i = 1.017$	$a = 0.5$ ml. $i = 1.037$	$a = 2.0$ ml. $i = 1.017$
15	0.1514	0.0313	0.1229	0.0341	0.1335	0.3370	0.0670	0.2735	0.0758	0.2974
16	07	11	22	38	25	54	93	19	52	50
17	0.1499	10	15	35	15	38	89	04	46	28
18	92	08	08	33	06	22	86	0.2690	41	06
19	86	06	02	31	0.1297	07	82	75	36	0.2886
20	79	05	0.1196	28	88	0.3292	78	62	31	66
21	72	03	90	26	79	78	75	48	26	48
22	66	02	83	24	70	63	71	34	21	28
23	59	00	77	22	62	48	68	20	16	08
24	53	0.0299	71	19	53	34	65	07	11	0.2790
25	46	97	65	17	45	20	61	0.2594	07	72
26	40	96	60	15	37	06	58	81	02	53
27	34	94	54	13	29	0.3193	55	69	0.0698	36
28	28	93	49	11	22	79	52	57	93	20
29	22	91	43	10	15	66	49	45	89	04
30	16	90	38	08	08	53	46	33	85	0.2688
31	11	89	33	06	01	40	43	22	82	74
32	05	88	28	05	0.1195	28	40	11	78	59
33	00	86	23	03	88	15	37	00	74	44
34	0.1394	85	18	01	82	03	34	0.2489	71	30

To obtain factors for a sample other than 1 ml., divide the above factors for 1 ml. by the milliliters of sample analyzed: e.g., for a 2-ml. sample, S, and a being the same, the factors are one-half of those for a 1-ml. sample.

It is necessary to perform a blank analysis for each type of determination—the $P_1 - P_2$ value constitutes the c correction.

Carbon dioxide content: For the carbon dioxide *content* of the serum, plasma, or whole blood, the specimen must be taken under albolene (mineral oil). For the carbon dioxide combining capacity, the specimen must be saturated with air containing 5.5% CO_2. See p. 25 of this chapter.

Procedure

The apparatus must be clean. Draw a drop of caprylic alcohol into the capillary above the cock at the top of the extraction chamber. Place 2.5 ml. of 0.1 N lactic acid (CO_2-free) in the cup. Run in 1 ml. of blood from a rubber-tipped pipette under lactic acid into the chamber. Wash in the sample with 2.5 ml. of lactic acid, giving a total of 3.5 ml. in the chamber and the capillary connecting cup. Seal the cock with mercury. Evacuate the apparatus by lowering the leveling bulb until the mercury is at the 50-ml. mark. Close the cock leading to the leveling bulb. Shake the reaction mixture for 2 minutes. Readmit mercury until the gas volume in the chamber is reduced to 2 ml. (meniscus of the solution is at the 2-ml. mark). Read the manometer for $-P_1$ millimeters.

Admit mercury from the leveling bulb until the gas volume has been reduced to about 5 ml. Place 2 ml. of air-free 1 N NaOH in the cup. Slowly run 1 ml. of NaOH into the chamber to absorb the CO_2. After alkali has been added, admit a few drops of mercury from the cup to dislodge any liquid adhering to the underside of the cock. Absorption should take about 30 seconds. After the CO_2 is absorbed, readmit mercury from the leveling bulb until the meniscus of solution is again at the 2-ml. *a* mark. Read the manometer for P_2. The pressure P of CO_2 is $P_1 - P_2 = c$. Consult Table III for calculation of the CO_2 content of the blood.

Carbon dioxide in plasma: With plasma or water solutions of carbonates a simpler technique may be used. In place of normal NaOH for absorption, pipette 0.2 ml. of 5 N NaOH into the cup. Add it to the contents of the chamber at slight negative pressure with the cock to the leveling bulb open. Read P_2 on the manometer with the solution at the 2-ml. *a* mark. Determine the c correction for the reagents used. Consult Table III for the factors for calculation of the CO_2 content.

Calculation

To express results as millimoles per liter, either use Table I or III or divide the volumes per cent of gas by 2.226.

Comments

Normal resting adult: 55–73 vol. % CO_2 or 23–31 mM $BHCO_3$. Mild acidosis, no pronounced symptoms: 40–55 vol. % or 17–23 mM. Moderate to severe acidosis, symptoms may be apparent: 30–40 vol. %, or 12–17 mM. Severe acidosis, symptoms of acid intoxication: below 30 vol. % or below 12 mM.

Increased in hyperventilation, vomiting, and alkalosis.

BIBLIOGRAPHY

1. Peters, J. P., and Van Slyke, D. D., *Quantitative Clinical Chemistry*, Vol. 2, Williams & Wilkins Co., Baltimore, 1932.
2. Reiner, M., *Manual of Clinical Chemistry*, Interscience Publishers, New York, 1941.

Chloride

Submitted by: OTTO SCHALES, Alton Ochsner Medical Foundation, New Orleans, Louisiana.

Checked by: MARSCHELLE H. POWER, Section of Biochemistry, Mayo Clinic, Rochester, Minnesota.
NELSON F. YOUNG, Department of Clinical Pathology and Hospital Laboratories, Medical College of Virginia, Richmond, Virginia.
JOSEPH BENOTTI, Pratt Diagnostic Clinic. New England Medical Center, Boston, Massachusetts.

Authors: O. SCHALES, and S. S. SCHALES, *J. Biol. Chem.* **140:** 879 (1941).

Principle

As with silver ions, chloride ions combine with mercuric ions, without forming a precipitate, however. Mercuric chloride is only very slightly dissociated, and the end point of the titration is recognized by the appearance of mercuric ions in the solution through the formation of a violet blue complex salt with diphenylcarbazone.

The mercurimetric determination of chloride has several operating advantages over the Volhard method (1), and the sudden appearance of an intense violet blue color makes it easy to recognize the end point. Results are accurate within 1% and the method is applicable to the determination of chloride in a variety of biological fluids, such as protein-free blood and serum filtrates, cerebrospinal fluids, and urine. Like silver nitrate, mercuric nitrate does not differentiate between chloride and bromide. In the titration of serum from patients with bromide poisoning, the result represents, therefore, the sum of the milliequivalents of chloride and bromide present.

Reagents

1. Mercuric nitrate solution: Place a few hundred milliliters of water in a 1000-ml. volumetric flask, add 20 ml. of 2 N nitric acid and 2.9–3.0 g. of mercuric nitrate (c.p. Baker's), and dissolve the salt by mixing. Fill to 1000 ml. with water and mix.

2. Indicator solution: Dissolve 100 mg. of s-diphenyl carbazone

(Eastman No. 4459) in 100 ml. of 95% alcohol, and store in the cold in a brown bottle. The orange-red solution must be protected from light, as it turns yellow when exposed to daylight for a few days and cannot be used. Even in the dark in the refrigerator a slow change takes place, and the solution does not give a sharp end point after about 2 months of storage. Consequently it is necessary to prepare a fresh solution each month.

3. *Chloride Standard:* Dry sodium chloride c.p. at 120° C., dissolve 584.5 mg. in water, and make up to 1000 ml. The solution contains 10 meq. of chloride per liter and is used for the standardization of each new batch of mercuric nitrate solution.

4. *Standardization of mercuric nitrate solution:* Titrate 2-ml. portions of the standard sodium chloride solution, as described for Folin-Wu serum filtrates. The mercuric nitrate solution is approximately $N/60$, so about 1.2 ml. is required for the titration of 2 ml. of chloride standard. For routine work a factor F may be calculated from the result of this titration. The amount of mercuric nitrate solution (expressed in milliliters) used for the titration of 2 ml. of Folin-Wu filtrate is multiplied by F to give the results in milliequivalents of chloride per liter of serum. F equals $100/Z$, where Z is the amount of mercuric nitrate solution used for the titration of 2 ml. of NaCl standard.

The standard mercuric nitrate solution is stable indefinitely and need not be protected from light.

Procedure

1. *Serum chloride:* To 2 ml. of Folin-Wu filtrate, (equivalent to 0.2 ml. of serum) in a 25-ml. Erlenmeyer flask add 0.06 ml. (4 drops) of indicator solution. Add mercuric nitrate from a burette calibrated in 0.01-ml. intervals. Hypodermic needles on the tips of the microburettes are unsatisfactory, as the metal reacts with the mercuric nitrate, causing serious errors. A fine glass tip should be used instead, delivering about 100 drops per milliliter. The clear solution becomes an intense violet blue on addition of the first drop of excess mercuric nitrate solution.

Serum may be titrated without previous removal of protein, but the end point is then only a pale violet, which can, however, be recognized without difficulty. If no deproteinization is carried out, add 0.2 ml. of serum to 1.8 ml. of water in a 25-ml. Erlenmeyer flask, and continue the analysis as described above. The results obtained with protein-free filtrates are 1–2 meq. lower than those obtained with untreated serum. This is probably due to a small loss of chloride by adsorption on the protein precipitate.

2. Cerebrospinal fluid chloride: To 1.8 ml. of water in a 25-ml. Erlenmeyer flask add 0.2 ml. of spinal fluid and 0.06 ml. (4 drops) of indicator solution. Carry out titration as described above. Because of the protein contents of spinal fluid, the formation of colored complexes (salmon red to violet) may occur in the beginning of the titration. These colors disappear as the titration is continued, and the solution becomes clear and colorless to pale yellow. At the end point there is a sharp change to intense violet.

3. Chloride in urine: Titrate 2 ml. of diluted urine (1:10) or Folin-Wu filtrate as described for serum. If the chloride concentration is very low, repeat the titration, using a larger volume of diluted urine. It is very important to see that the urine sample is not alkaline at the start of the titration. The additon of mercuric nitrate solution to a mixture of diluted alkaline urine and indicator solution results in the immediate appearance of a pink color which would mask the end point. This disturbing color is easily removed by the addition of a few drops (0.02 ml. each) of dilute (approximately 1 N) nitric acid. Then the titration can be carried out satisfactorily. Care should be taken to avoid an excess of acid. Add only enough to just remove the disturbing color, which brings the pH of the mixture to about 6. In stronger acid solution the indicator loses sensitivity.

Normal Values:

1. 99–111 meq. chloride per liter serum.
2. 77–88 meq. chloride per liter whole blood.
3. 125–135 meq. chloride per liter cerebrospinal fluid.

The chloride concentration in urine varies with the dietary intake. On a normal (not salt-free) diet, a normal adult excretes about 170–250 meq. of chloride during a period of 24 hours.

Comments

This method has been used routinely and has been found to be satisfactory on serum, urine, and cerebrospinal fluid. The results reported here were obtained chiefly on blood donors with no indication of illness.   The sera were run without deproteinizing, and the urines were slightly acidified with HNO_3 when indicated.

Results of 100 normal sera:

(a) *Average value:* 102.7 meq./l. chloride.

(b) Five of the 100 sera showed 2% difference in duplicates. The other 95 were 1% or less.

(c) Ninety-eight values fell between 99 and 110 meq./l. (2 values were 95–96 and 97–98).

(d) Recoveries on 6 normal sera (0.1 ml. of serum + 0.1 ml. of NaCl containing 110 meq./l. averaged 99.6%, with a range of 98–101%.

Recoveries on Cerebrospinal Fluid and Urine:

(a) Five urines containing 8–170 meq./l. gave 101% recovery of 0.1 ml. of standard NaCl used above, with a range of 98–102%.

(b) Recoveries on 6 cerebrospinal fluid samples containing 98–130 meq./l. gave 100.2% with the same amount of standard NaCl added to 0.1-ml. samples with a range of 99.5–101.2%.

Mercurimetric titration of tungstic acid filtrate prepared essentially according to the directions of Folin and Wu has given excellent results in another series in comparison with analysis by the Wilson-Ball method.   The results are shown in Table I.   In these comparisons duplicate samples for preparation of the filtrates and for the Wilson-Ball procedure were measured out at the same time with the same 1-ml. syringe pipette.   Likewise, samples of sodium chloride standard were measured with the same pipette for both procedures.

The Folin-Wu filtrates were prepared in 15-ml. centrifuge tubes, in 1:10 dilution, using 0.5 ml. each of 10% sodium tungstate and 0.67 N sulfuric acid.   The latter was added last, the mixture was thoroughly mixed by means of a stirring rod, the tube was capped, and after about 30 minutes it was centrifuged.   Two-milliliter portions of the clear supernatant were titrated with mercury by means of a syringe-controlled air-driven burette of about 1.4–ml. capacity. This method of titration may make possible a somewhat more consistent end point than the drop method from a burette with stopcock.   Standards were treated exactly like the unknowns, including the addition of tungstate and acid.

TABLE I

COMPARISON OF WILSON-BALL AND MERCURIMETRIC METHODS

(Results in milliequivalents per liter)

Material analyzed	Mercurimetric titration	Wilson-Ball method
1. Serum, pool A	104.5	104.1
	104.0	103.9
2. Heparin plasma (Patient K)	104.2	104.1
	104.5	104.1
3. Serum, pool B	100.5	101.0
	100.3	101.2
4. Heparin plasma (Patient H)	94.3	95.1
	94.3	95.2
5. Oxalate plasma (pooled)	102.7	101.7
	102.5	102.0
6. Oxalate plasma (Patient S)	106.0	105.1
	106.0	105.1
7. Oxalate plasma (Patient M)	104.1	103.5
	104.2	103.5
8. Serum (anemia)	108.1	108.2
	108.0	108.2
9. Serum (Patient X)	103.5	103.1
	103.5	103.1
10. Serum (Patient Y)	103.0	102.5
	102.8	102.5
11. Urine (Patient A)		
1	54.9	52.4
2	59.4	55.8
3	57.2	56.4
4	54.7	52.8
12. Urine (Patient H)		
5	44.1	42.1
6	35.4	34.7
7	35.8	34.1
13. Urine (Patient T)		
8	16.2	13.2
9	23.2	20.4
10	26.2	21.8
14. Urine (Patient H)		
11	29.6	29.3
12	37.3	35.8

The results shown in Table I indicate that mercurimetric values in urine, especially of specimens preserved in the refrigerator more than a day or so, are very likely to be high. Analysis number 11 was done on a fresh 24-hour specimen; 12 had been preserved in refrigerator 2 days with added thymol; samples 8, 9, and 10 had been similarly preserved for about 8 weeks; 1, 2, 3, and 4 for 2 weeks; and 5, 6, and 7 for 1 week.

In general, the older the specimen, the higher is the value by mercury as compared to Wilson-Ball. In the case of the older specimens perhaps the adjustment of acidity was not so satisfactory, as they may have had more ammonia or other interfering substances in solution compared to fresh specimens, so that the mercury titration should not have been applied to them.

BIBLIOGRAPHY

1. Volhard, J., *J. prakt. Chem.* **9**: 217 (1874); *Z. Anal. Chem.* **17**: 482 (1878).

Total and Free Cholesterol

Submitted by: MARGARET M. KASER, Veterans Administration Center, Wood, Wisconsin.

Checked by: LOUIS B. DOTTI, Saint Luke's Hospital, New York, New York.

Authors: R. SCHOENHEIMER and W. M. SPERRY, *J. Biol. Chem.* **106:** 745 (1934).
W. M. SPERRY and M. WEBB, *J. Biol. Chem.* **187:** 97, (1950).

Principle

Serum is treated with acetone-ethanol to remove the proteins and extract the lipids. For the determination of free cholesterol an aliquot of the extract is acidified with acetic acid and digitonin is added, which precipitates free cholesterol as the digitonide. For the estimation of total cholesterol a preliminary saponification of the esterified cholesterol with potassium hydroxide is necessary, after which the total cholesterol is precipitated in the same manner as the free cholesterol. The precipitates are washed, dried, and dissolved in glacial acetic acid. Acetic anhydride-sulfuric acid reagent is added (Liebermann-Burchard reaction), and the tubes are incubated in the dark at a controlled temperature for a measured period of time. The colors developed are compared in a photoelectric colorimeter with that of a cholesterol standard similarly treated, by measurement of the absorption at 625 mμ or with a red filter.

Reagents

Only reagent grade chemicals should be used.

1. Solvents: Acetone-absolute ethanol, 1:1; acetone-ether, 1:2; ether.

It is recommended that the solvents used be redistilled. The ether must be peroxide-free; it may be tested by shaking 5–10 ml. with a solution of pure ferrous sulfate and potassium or sodium thiocyanate in a glass-stoppered cylinder. A red color due to the formation of ferric thiocyanate indicates the presence of peroxides.

It is advisable to make certain that there is no color with the reagents alone.   If this test is positive, the ether should be redistilled.

2. Digitonin solution: Dissolve 500 mg. of digitonin in 100 ml. of 50% alcohol (55 ml. of 95% alcohol and 45 ml. of distilled water) at 60° C.

3. Potassium hydroxide solution: Dissolve 10 g. of potassium hydroxide in 20 ml. of distilled water.   Filter through a sintered glass filter before use if a sediment develops.

4. Acetic acid: Dilute 10 ml. of glacial acetic acid to 100 ml. with distilled water.

5. Acetic anhydride, 99–100%.

6. Cholesterol solution, 1 mg./ml.: Dissolve 100 mg. of pure anhydrous cholesterol in 100 ml. of glacial acetic acid.   Suitable working standards may be made by dilution of this solution.

Cholesterol does not keep well under ordinary conditions of storage and should be recrystallized.   This may be done by dissolving 1 or 2 g. of cholesterol in as little hot absolute ethanol as is required to dissolve it completely.   Then set the solution aside to cool. Collect the crystals of cholesterol, which separate upon standing, on a small Buchner filter, wash them several times with small quantities of absolute ethanol, and dry by suction.   Keep the crystals in a vacuum desiccator over sulfuric acid or phosphorus pentoxide.

Special equipment

1. Small funnels of about 30-ml. capacity.

2. Filter paper.   This must be a rapid, lipid-free paper such as Schleicher and Schull's Sharkskin paper.   It is advisable to extract it with hot alcohol.

3. Stirring rods, approximately 13 cm. long and 3 mm. in diameter.

4. Quart-size preserving jars with screw caps.

5. Dropping bottles with ground-in pipettes fitted with rubber bulbs.

6. Centrifuge tubes, Pyrex, heavy-duty, 12 ml.

7. Water bath with test tube racks and thermometer.

Procedure

1. Extraction of blood serum: A glass-stoppered 25-ml. volumetric flask is filled about half-way with acetone-ethanol, and 1 ml. of serum is carefully measured and added slowly with rotation of the flask. A finely divided precipitate should result. The flask is immersed in water, which has been heated to boiling, and agitated to prevent bumping until the solvent is brought just to a boil. *Caution:* There should be no open flames! After the flask has cooled, acetone-ethanol is added to the mark, the glass stopper is inserted, and the contents are throughly mixed and filtered through a rapid filter paper into a test tube. Aliquots of the filtrate are taken for the determination of free and of total cholesterol. Measurements should be made at once, and the flask should be kept stoppered to prevent evaporation.

2. Precipitation of free cholesterol: To 6 ml. of the filtrate in a 12-ml., heavy-duty Pyrex centrifuge tube are added 3 drops of the acetic acid solution and 3 ml. of the digitonin solution. The mixture is stirred thoroughly with a stirring rod, which is left in the tube. The tube is placed in a preserving jar, the bottom of which is covered with a layer of sand about 2 in. deep to support the tubes, and the jar is closed tightly and left overnight at room temperature.

The next day any precipitate adhering to the wall of the centrifuge tube near the surface of the liquid is gently freed and returned to the solution with the stirring rod, the rod is drained against the side of the tube just above the liquid, and it is then removed without contact with the upper part of the tube and placed on a special rack. The rack may be made of heavy wire or metal and is designed to hold a number of stirring rods, so that they may be held without danger of touching each other or of rubbing off any adhering precipitate. The position of each rod is noted, so that it is always returned to its proper tube. The tube is centrifuged about 15 minutes at about 2800 r.p.m. The supernatant liquid, which should be clear except for the occasional presence of a few particles floating near the surface, is carefully decanted with a single, slow inversion, so that none of the precipitate is lost. The tube is drained for a few minutes in a beaker, the bottom of which is covered with a fresh piece of acid-washed filter paper. The stirring rod is returned to the tube, and about 3 ml. of acetone-ether are added from the pipette of a dropping bottle and used to rinse the rod and the sides of the tube. The contents of the tube are stirred thoroughly, the rod is drained against the side of the tube and returned to the rack, the tube is centrifuged, and the supernatant fluid is decanted as before. The precipitate is washed twice more in the same manner except that ether is substituted for the acetone-ether. The rod is left in the tube. If desired, the tube may be kept at this stage for several days.

3. Precipitation of total cholesterol: Three drops of the potassium hydroxide solution is placed in a dry, heavy-duty centrifuge tube with 3 ml. of the serum extract, and the mixture is stirred vigorously with a stirring rod until no droplets of alkali remain in the tip of the tube. A preserving jar with sufficient sand in the bottom to support centrifuge tubes is kept in an incubator at 38–40° C. The tube is placed in the sand, and the jar is tightly covered and placed in the incubator for at least 30 minutes.

The tube is removed from the jar and cooled. Three milliliters of the acetone-ethanol solution and a drop of 1% phenolphthalein in 95% alcohol are added. Ten per cent acetic acid is added, a drop at a time, and mixed well with the contents of the tube by means of the stirring rod until the pink color of phenolphthalein disappears. This should require from 12 to 18 drops. Three extra drops of acetic acid and 3 ml. of digitonin solution are added, and the sample is treated as described for free cholesterol, except that the precipitate is washed with ether only once.

4. Development and reading of color: The tubes are placed in the order in which they are to be read in a sand bath at 110–115° C., which is then returned to a drying oven at that temperature for 30 minutes. A water bath with a temperature of 25° C. is prepared, which must be maintained at that temperature during the rest of the procedure by the addition of hot or cold water as required. The sand bath is removed from the oven, and 3 ml. of pure glacial acetic acid is added to the first tube and stirred vigorously. The tube is returned immediately to the hot sand while acid is being added to the next two or three tubes, 2 or 3 minutes in all. The solution is stirred again, and the tube is removed from the sand, cooled, and placed in the water bath. The process is continued until all the tubes are in the water bath in the order of reading. A tube containing 3 ml. of dilute standard solution of a concentration of 0.1 mg. of cholesterol per milliliter is placed at the beginning of the series and another at the end; a blank tube with 3 ml. of glacial acetic acid is also prepared.

The reagent for the development of color is prepared just before use and in sufficient quantity for all the unknown tubes, the standards, and a blank. This is conveniently done in a glass-stoppered graduate or bottle, which is chilled in an ice bath. With the graduate still in the ice bath and containing the required amount of acetic anhydride, 1 ml. of concentrated sulfuric acid is added for each 20 ml. of acetic anhydride and mixed during the addition. The stopper is then inserted, and the graduate is removed from the bath, shaken vigorously for a few moments, and returned to the bath.

About 10 minutes later, when the reagent is thoroughly chilled, the first tube is removed from the 25° C. water bath and wiped dry, 6 ml. of the acetic anhydride-sulfuric acid reagent is added, the contents of the tube are stirred vigorously, and the rod is removed. The tube is returned to the water bath, or if the readings are to be made in a photometer which uses matched cuvettes of the test tube type, the solution is poured into a cuvette, which is placed in the 25° C. water bath. The process is repeated in the order of reading for each tube of the series, and the time required should be carefully adjusted so that the time elapsing between the addition of the acetic anhydride-sulfuric acid reagent and the reading will be the same for all tubes, preferably 30–31 minutes, although the color is fairly stable from 27 to 37 minutes, when the intensity of the color is at its maximum. As soon as the reagent has been added to all the tubes and the tubes have been replaced in the water bath, they are placed in a dark place, such as a cupboard, for the rest of the time interval, but care should be taken that the temperature of the water bath is maintained. The galvanometer of the photometer is adjusted to 100% transmittance or zero optical density at 625 mμ or with a red filter with the blank tube, and the unknown samples and the standards are then read at the proper interval after the addition of the reagent.

Calculation

If the conditions described above for the development of the color are carefully followed, the intensities obtained with given amounts of cholesterol are quite constant, and it is possible to establish a calibration curve relating transmittance or optical density readings to concentrations. However, it is advisable to include one or more standard tubes in each series of determinations in order to be certain that the calibration curve is still valid.

A calibration curve may be prepared as follows. Two dilute cholesterol solutions are made by diluting 6 ml. of the standard cholesterol solution (1 mg./ml.) to 50 ml. with glacial acetic acid in a 50-ml. volumetric flask (I), and 12 ml. to 50 ml. (II). These solutions are used to prepare a series of test tubes or cuvettes containing known amounts of cholesterol. The table below lists the volumes of the two standards with the volumes of glacial acetic acid required to give a total volume of 3 ml. in each tube, the number of milligrams of cholesterol in each tube, and the equivalent concentration of total serum cholesterol.

Standard, ml.	Acetic acid, ml.	Cholesterol, mg.	Total serum cholesterol, mg./100 ml.
I 0.5	2.5	0.06	50
1.0	2.0	0.12	100
1.5	1.5	0.18	150
2.0	1.0	0.24	200
2.5	0.5	0.30	250
3.0	0	0.36	300
II 2.0	1.0	0.48	400
2.5	0.5	0.60	500
3.0	0	0.72	600

The corresponding values for free cholesterol are one-half the figures for total cholesterol. It is advisable not to extend the curve below a transmission reading of about 30% or above an optical density of about 0.523. If serum samples are encountered which give readings outside this range, the determinations should be repeated, using smaller aliquots of serum.

In the experience of Schoenheimer and Sperry, the color developed by the Liebermann-Burchard reaction follows Beer's law; i.e., the ratios of the concentrations of cholesterol to the corresponding optical densities approach a constant. If this is found to be the case, one is justified in calculating unknown values from the optical density of a single standard, such as that suggested in the description of the method, instead of employing a calibration curve. The calculations are then as follows:

$$\frac{\text{Density of unknown}}{\text{Density of standard}} \times \frac{\text{mg. cholesterol in standard}}{\text{ml. of extract used}} \times$$

$$\frac{\text{total volume of extract}}{\text{ml. of serum used}} \times 100 = \text{Mg. total cholesterol per 100 ml. serum}$$

Substituting the figures which apply to the method described here, the formula becomes:

$$\frac{\text{Density of unknown}}{\text{Density of standard}} \times \frac{0.3}{3} \times \frac{25}{1} \times 100 = \text{Mg. total cholesterol per 100 ml. serum}$$

For free cholesterol the calculation is similar:

$$\frac{\text{Density of unknown}}{\text{Density of standard}} \times \frac{0.3}{6} \times \frac{25}{1} \times 100 = \text{Mg. free cholesterol per 100 ml. serum}$$

Comments

The procedure described above is capable of a high degree of accuracy and excellent reproducibility, provided that the details of the method are carefully followed. The volume of the colored solution should be adequate for most of the photoelectric colorimeters in common use. However, if necessary, the procedure may be varied if the following conditions are met: (1) the volume of serum in the total volume of extract may be decreased; in fact, this is desirable if the total cholesterol is above about 600 mg. per 100 ml. of serum; the volume of serum used must not exceed 1/25 of the total volume of extract; (2) the volume of extract from which the total cholesterol is precipitated may be varied provided that one drop of potassium hydroxide solution is added for each milliliter of extract and 1 ml. of digitonin solution is used for each 2 ml. of acetone-ethanol; (3) the volume in which color is developed may be altered without reference to the volume of extract from which the cholesterol is precipitated, but 2 ml. of the acetic anhydride-sulfuric acid reagent are added for each 1 ml. of acetic acid solution.

Traces of water interfere with color development. The bottles of sulfuric acid, acetic anhydride, and glacial acetic acid, which readily take up moisture from the air, must be kept tightly closed when not in use. The cholesterol digitonide precipitate must be completely dry, and when the acetic anhydride-sulfuric acid reagent and the colorimeter cuvettes are in water or ice baths care must be taken that contamination with water does not occur.

Normal Values

The level of the serum cholesterol in a given person remains quite constant, although there are a number of metabolic processes which might be expected to affect it. Since cholesterol is a constituent of all mixed diets, dietary intake is one factor which may conceivably affect the blood level. This possibility will be discussed below. Furthermore, it has been realized for some time that cholesterol is synthesized by the liver, but it is only comparatively recently that Bloch and Rittenberg (3, 4, 5) have demonstrated that the chief building block for the formation of cholesterol is acetic acid, which may arise from a variety of metabolic pathways, but primarily from the catabolism of fatty acids. The most important site of synthesis is the liver, which also esterifies cholesterol. The liver excretes cholesterol in the bile, and it is responsible for the storage and probably for the destruction of cholesterol. Cholesterol gives rise to the cholic acid portion of the bile acids elaborated by the liver (6), and, although the evidence is as yet incomplete, it is reasonable to suppose that it may be a precursor of such structurally related compounds as the hormones of the adrenal cortex and the sex glands. Little is known concerning the reactions involved in the various metabolic pathways in which cholesterol takes part and the mechanisms by which they are regulated. Any increase in our understanding of the significance of cholesterol determinations must await advances in our knowledge in some of these areas.

The range of normal serum cholesterol values is very wide, but the level for each individual shows little fluctuation. Although it is frequently stated that the normal total serum cholesterol is not related to age, it would appear from the recent report of Keys, Mickelsen, Miller, Hayes, and Todd (7) that this is the most important physiological variable to be considered. These authors have reviewed the literature and have presented their own studies of over 2000 carefully selected healthy individuals. This is the only series sufficiently large to establish firmly the presence or absence of a correlation between serum cholesterol and age, but the work of other investigators, such as the data of Page, Kirk, Lewis, Thompson, and Van Slyke (8), is consistent with the findings in this more extensive study. Keys et al. (7) agree with others in finding no evidence of a sex difference. The table below is adapted from their data. Under the heading "Population limits" are the limits within which the total cholesterol values of 90% and 98% of the population of a given age will be found.

		Population limits			
Age	Mean	90%		98%	
18	168.2	118	219	97	240
20	173.7	121	226	99	248
25	184.4	128	240	105	264
30	195.1	129	261	101	289
35	200.·.	128	272	97	303
40	219.4	154	284	127	312
45	235.5	174	297	147	324
50	248.3	174	323	142	354
55	255.7	180	332	148	364
60	253.3	197	309	173	333
65	236.7	179	294	154	320
70	224.6	155	294	124	325
75	211.8	148	276	118	306

The proportion of the total cholesterol which is present as free cholesterol is very constant in healthy individuals and seems to be unaffected by age (9). The range of normal variation found by this procedure is about 24–32% free cholesterol, but fluctuation of the ratio of the free to total cholesterol in a given healthy individual is even less than this (1, 9).

The ingestion of ordinary meals has little, if any, influence on the serum cholesterol (9, 10). Even the feeding of cholesterol itself seems to be without effect with the exception of a few reports in which excessively large amounts were used.

Pathological Values

In view of the wide range of normal values found for total cholesterol and the relative constancy of each individual level, a deviation from normal can be detected more readily if the usual value for a given person is known, although the figure in question may still be within the range of normal variation. The age of the subject should also be taken into account, as indicated in the preceding section. The importance of an appreciation of the range of normal values as related to age is apparent in any discussion of the significance of serum cholesterol in the development of human atherosclerosis, since diseases of the cardiovascular system are leading causes of disability and death in the middle-age and older age groups. There has been a tendency to incriminate high serum cholesterol levels as a causative factor, although the literature is inconclusive on this point (10). Findings of elevated values for serum cholesterol in patients with these conditions must be interpreted in the light of the higher levels to be found in the age groups most subject to these diseases. Likewise, the possible significance of dietary cholesterol as an etiologic agent appears to be minimized by the difficulty encountered in producing changes in serum cholesterol levels by the ingestion of meals containing large amounts of lipids or by the administration of cholesterol to human subjects (10). Furthermore, several recent studies in which attention has been focused on the dietary habits of groups of subjects have demonstrated a lack of correlation between serum cholesterol and the level of fat and cholesterol intake (11, 12, 13), except with diets that are completely free of fat (12). Of interest is the demonstration that the synthesis of cholesterol from acetate, which proceeds at a maximum rate in the liver (14, 15), also occurs in the rat at a slower rate in other tissues and organs as well as in the aortas of chickens and rabbits (17). However, the cholesterol of the adult central nervous system is fixed and does not take part in any metabolic reactions (16). Recent investigations of the relationships between the various lipid fractions of serum (18), of the state of dispersion of the lipids (19), and of the physical-chemical nature of the lipoprotein complexes (20, 21, 22) in cardiovascular diseases are indicative of a growing realization of the complexity of the problem presented by atherosclerosis.

The occurrence of abnormal cholesterol levels in other conditions is less controversial and is discussed in other sources. The literature has been very well reviewed by Peters and Van Slyke (10). Cholesterol shares the marked elevations observed in the lipids in uncontrolled diabetes. This appears to be directly related not to the severity of the disease but, rather, to the mobilization of lipids from the body stores in the absence of, or with extreme impairment of, the metabolism of carbohydrate. Similarly, increases may be observed in conditions in which starvation for carbohydrate occurs, as in patients who are unable to take nourishment by mouth. This can be corrected by the oral or parenteral administration of carbohydrate. The mechanism by which plasma cholesterol, as well as other lipids, may reach extremely high levels in the nephrotic syndrome is not understood. However, values as high as 1 g. per 100 ml. or higher may occur, especially in patients with severe edema, pronounced albuminuria and marked depression of serum albumin. Little, if any, characteristic disturbance of plasma cholesterol occurs in other renal diseases. Total serum cholesterol values in diseases of the liver are increased or decreased depending upon the nature and duration of the condition. Furthermore, it is only in diseases of the liver and biliary tract and in acute infections that deviations from the usual constant ratio of free to total cholesterol occur (1). Quite marked elevation of the serum cholesterol occurs in obstructive jaundice (10). On the other hand, in diseases affecting the liver parenchyma or in obstructive jaundice of long duration, the synthesis of cholesterol and its esterification may be impaired to a greater or lesser degree, and with severe conditions the values for total cholesterol may be well below the normal range with very little ester. Inasmuch as most liver diseases exhibit some degree of biliary obstruction and more or less cellular injury, correct interpretation of the serum total and free cholesterol levels may be difficult. However, these determinations, if repeated at intervals, can be of aid in diagnosis and prognosis.

The tendency of the serum cholesterol to vary inversely with the basal metabolic rate has made its estimation useful in the study of conditions of abnormal thyroid function. Thus, in hyperthyroidism, values in the lower portions of the range of normal values or below normal may occur, and, conversely, hypothyroidism frequently exhibits an increased serum cholesterol. However, because of the wide range of normal values and the overlapping of the normal and abnormal figures in these conditions, serum cholesterol is usually regarded as being only an aid to diagnosis to be interpreted in relation to the basal metabolic rate. Of course, if a patient's serum cholesterol before the onset of thyroid disease or the initiation of therapy is known, a deviation can be more readily detected, and the determination assumes increased significance.

Marked elevations of serum cholesterol are found in some, but not all, lipoidoses or xanthomatoses, in which abnormal deposits of lipids occur in the body, particularly in the reticulo-endothelial system, the skin, and the tendons. In some, the deposits are largely cholesterol and are accompanied by a hypercholesterolemia. In some, other lipids are involved. These diseases are distinguished largely on the basis of the lipids concerned, but nothing is known concerning their etiology. In addition, there is a condition known as essential or idiopathic lipemia, in which extreme increases of all the plasma lipid fractions, including cholesterol, are found, but, again, the cause of the condition is obscure.

Serum cholesterol, although not affected appreciably by variations in dietary intake, may be low in wasting diseases, such as the terminal stage of cancer and tuberculous infections. In part, this may be due to a decreased synthesis and esterification by the liver. Because of the malnutrition common to these conditions, the reports of Keys et al. (12) are pertinent that the serum cholesterol is reduced in subjects deprived of fat, which is the chief source of acetate residues from which cholesterol may be synthesized.

BIBLIOGRAPHY

1. Sperry, W. M., and Webb, M., J. Biol. Chem. 187: 97 (1950).
2. Schoenheimer, R., and Sperry, W. M., J. Biol. Chem. 106: 745 (1934).
3. Bloch, K., and Rittenberg, D., J. Biol. Chem. 143: 297 (1942).
4. Bloch, K., and Rittenberg, D., J. Biol. Chem. 145: 625 (1942).
5. Bloch, K., and Rittenberg, D., J. Biol. Chem. 155: 243 (1944).
6. Bloch, K., Berg, B. N., and Rittenberg, D., J. Biol. Chem. 149: 511 (1943).
7. Keys, A., Mickelsen, O., Miller, E. v. O., Hayes, E. R., and Todd, R. L., J. Clin. Invest. 29: 1347 (1950).
8. Page, I. H., Kirk, E., Lewis, W. H., Thompson, W. R., and Van Slyke, D. D., J. Biol. Chem. 111: 613 (1935).
9. Sperry, W. M., J. Biol. Chem. 114: 125 (1936).
10. Peters, J. P., and Van Slyke, D. D., Quantitative Clinical Chemistry, 2nd ed., Vol. 1, pp. 373–589, Williams & Wilkins, Baltimore, 1946.
11. Wilkinson, C. F., Blecha, E., and Reimer, A., Arch. Internal Med. 85: 389 (1950).
12. Keys, A., Mickelsen, O., Miller, E. v. O., and Chapman, C. B., Science 112: 79 (1950).
13. Gertler, M. M., Garn, S. M., and White, P. D., Circulation 2: 696 (1950).
14. Borek, E., and Rittenberg, D., J. Biol. Chem. 179: 843 (1949).
15. Bloch, K., Circulation 1: 214 (1950).
16. Srere, P. A., Chaikoff, I. L., Treitman, S. S., and Burstein, L. S., J. Biol. Chem. 182: 629 (1950).
17. Siperstein, M. D., Chaikoff, I. L., and Chernick, S. S., Science 113: 747 (1951).
18. Gertler, M. M., and Garn, S. M., Science 112: 14 (1950).
19. Moreton, J. R., Science 106: 190 (1947).
20. Müller, E., Zentr. allgem. Pathol. u. pathol. Anat. 85: 300 (1949).
21. Gofman, J. W., Lindgren, F., Elliott, H., Mantz, W., Hewitt, J., Strisower, B., Herring, V., and Lyon, T. P., Science 111: 166 (1950).
22. Gofman, J. W., Jones, H. B., Lindgren, F. T., Lyon, T. P., Elliott, H. A., and Strisower, B., Circulation 2: 161 (1950).

Creatinine

Submitted by: GEORGE R. KINGSLEY and R. R. SCHAFFERT, Veterans Administration Center, Los Angeles, California.

Checked by: MIRIAM REINER, Gallinger Municipal Hospital, Washington, D. C

Authors: S. R. BENEDICT and J. A. BEHRE, J. Biol. Chem. 114: 515 (1936).
L. C. CLARK and H. L. THOMPSON, Anal. Chem. 21: 1218 (1949).

Principle

Serum creatinine, in a protein-free filtrate, is determined by its reaction with alkaline picrate to form a yellow-red color, the Jaffe reaction (1). Although this reaction is not specific for creatinine, fortunately practically all the chromogenic material in serum appears to be creatinine. It has been shown that material absorbed on and released from Lloyd's reagent and giving the Jaffe reaction is isolated as creatinine (2). Alkaline dinitrobenzoate (3) has been used instead of alkaline picrate in the Jaffe reaction and has given values practically identical to those obtained after absorption of the creatinine upon Lloyd's reagent (4). Creatinine has been determined accurately by the application of optimum hydrogen ion concentration, correct concentration of reagents, and time of color development in the alkaline picrate method (5).

I. ALKALINE PICRATE METHOD

Reagents

1. *Acid tungstate.* Add 38.7 ml. of conc. sulfuric acid c.p. to 18 l. of distilled water, mix thoroughly, and titrate to 0.074 N. Add and dissolve 207 g. of sodium tungstate c.p. The final mixture should have a pH of 2.1–2.2. Keep free of CO_2.

2. *Recrystallized picric acid.* Purify picric acid c.p. by recrystallizing twice from glacial acetic acid and drying at room temperature (1 g. picric acid to 1.5 ml. acetic acid at 100°C. filter hot).

3. *Sodium picrate buffer.* Dissolve 11.7 g. of recrystallized picric acid in about 900 ml. of distilled water, and adjust to a pH of 2.0

55

with 2 N NaOH. Let stand overnight, and again adjust pH to
2.0. Then dilute to 1 l.

   4. Sodium hydroxide.   2.5 N NaOH.

   5. Alkaline picrate.   Mix 9 parts of sodium picrate buffer with 1
part of 10% sodium hydroxide. *Prepare fresh just before use.*

   6. Creatinine stock standard.   Dissolve 0.100 g. of creatinine in 0.1
N hydrochloric acid and dilute to 100 ml. in a volumetric flask with
0.1 N hydrochloric acid.

   7. Creatinine working standard.   Dilute 1 ml. of creatinine stock
standard to 100 ml. with distilled water. Add a few drops of chloroform and mix (5 ml. = 0.05 mg.).

   STANDARDIZATION: Dilute 1, 2, 3, 4, and 5 ml. of dilute creatinine
working standard to 5 ml. with distilled water, and treat as directed
for *blood filtrate* under Procedure for creatinine.

Procedure

   1. Serum: Add 1 ml. of serum to a 20-ml. centrifuge tube containing 7 ml. of acid tungstate reagent and 2 ml. of distilled water.
Stopper the tube, and mix by inversion several times. Do not
shake. Centrifuge at 2000 r.p.m. for 5 minutes. Prepare a *blank*
filtrate by mixing 4 ml. of acid tungstate and 6 ml. of distilled
water. Measure 5 ml. of the serum and blank centrifugate into
two photometer cuvettes, and add to each 2.5 ml. of alkaline picrate.
Mix. Let stand 15 minutes at room temperature. Read within
5 minutes in photometer after 100% transmission has been set with
reagent blank at 500 mμ.

   2. Urine: Add 1 ml. of a 1:50 dilution of urine to 5 ml. of alkaline
picrate. Dilute to 15 ml. with distilled water, let stand 15 minutes
for color development, and continue as described for serum.

Calculation

   Serum: Mg. creatinine per 100 ml. = K^* (2 − log %T).

   Urine: G. per 24 hours =

$$\frac{\text{24-hour urine vol. (ml.) } [K^*(2 - \log \%T)]}{2000}.$$

   * For transmissions between 100 and 57, K = 12.2. (Coleman spectrophotome-
ter No. 6 and No. 14, cuvette 6–304B).
   * For transmissions between 57 and 20, K = 13.5. (Coleman spectrophotometer
No. 6 and No. 14, cuvette 6–304B).

II. 3,5-DINITROBENZOIC ACID METHOD

Reagents

1. 3,5-Dinitrobenzoic acid reagent, 10% (6). Add 10 g. of 3.5% dinitrobenzoic acid to 25 ml. of 10% sodium carbonate, and mix. Add 75 ml. of distilled water to dissolve. Warm if necessary, and dilute to 100 ml. Filter. A pale yellow solution should be obtained.

2. 1.333 N sulfuric acid. Add and mix slowly 40 ml. of c.p. conc. sulfuric acid to 1000 ml. of distilled water. Titrate against 1.00 *N* NaOH with phenolphthalein as indicator.

3. 20% c.p. sodium tungstate. Keep in Pyrex or polyethylene bottle.

4. 2.5 N sodium hydroxide.

5. Stock creatinine standard. Dissolve 100 mg. of c.p. creatinine in and dilute to 100 ml. with 0.1 *N* HCl.

6. Creatinine working standard. Dilute 2 ml. of stock standard to 100 ml. with distilled water. Add a few drops of chloroform and mix (5 ml. = 0.10 mg.).

STANDARDIZATION: Dilute 1, 2, 3, 4, and 5 ml. of creatinine working standard to 5 ml., and proceed as described below for 5 ml. of blood tungstic acid filtrates.

Procedure

1. Blood: Add 2 ml. of whole blood to 6 ml. of distilled water in a large test tube. Mix until hemolysis is complete. Add, drop by drop, 1 ml. of 1.333 *N* sulfuric acid with constant mixing. Add 1 ml. of 20% sodium tungstate drop by drop while rotating the test tube, and then shake vigorously. Centrifuge at 2500 r.p.m. for 5 minutes. Place 5 ml. of centrifugate in a cuvette, and 5 ml. of distilled water in another cuvette for reagent blank. Add to each cuvette 1 drop of 2.5 *N* sodium hydroxide. Then add 1.5 ml. of 3,5-dinitrobenzoic acid reagent, and mix. Add 0.25 ml. of 2.5 *N* sodium hydroxide, and mix. Let stand in the dark at room temperature for 10 minutes. Set the reagent blank cuvette at 100% transmission in a photometer with 500-mμ light transmission or filter. Read the unknown within 1 minute.

2. Urine: Add 1 ml. of a 1:50 dilution of urine to 4 ml. of distilled water. Add 1 drop of 2.5 *N* sodium hydroxide, and continue as directed above for blood.

Calculation

Blood: Mg. creatinine per 100 ml. $= K^* (2 - \log \%T)$.

Urine: G. per 24 hours $=$

$$\frac{\text{24-hour urine vol. (ml.) } [K^*(2 - \log \%T)]}{2000}.$$

Normal Values (7)

1. Whole blood:

ALKALINE PICRATE METHOD: Mg. per 100 ml. $= 0.73–1.30$, av. 1.00.
DINITROBENZOIC ACID METHOD: Mg. per 100 ml. $= 0.62–1.05$, av. 0.81.

2. Serum:

ALKALINE PICRATE METHOD: Mg. per 100 ml. $= 0.61–1.10$, av. 0.84.
DINITROBENZOIC ACID METHOD: Mg. per 100 ml. $= 0.62–1.18$, av. 0.80.

Abnormal Values

Elevation of blood creatinine is primarily associated with renal disease and may rise to 20 mg. $\%$. It rarely exceeds this level.

Precautions and Notes

The color produced in the alkaline picrate method does not obey Beer's law, but fairly accurate results are obtained if two K constants are used, one from 100 to 57% transmission and the other from 57 to 20% transmission. The color is stable for only 5 minutes after full development.

The color produced by the dinitrobenzoic acid method is linear but is stable for only 1 minute.

Temperature has an appreciable effect on the rate of color development and its intensity. Determinations of creatinine should be made at approximately the same temperature at which the method is standardized.

A control standard should be run with each series of determinations as a check on reagents, temperature, photometer, technique, etc.

* $K = 16.6$ for Coleman junior spectrophotometer No. 6, (cuvette 6–304B).

BIBLIOGRAPHY

1. Jaffe, M., *Hoppe-Seyler's Z. physiol. Chem.* **10:** 391 (1886).
2. Gaebler, O. H., *J. Biol. Chem.* **89:** 451 (1930).
3. Benedict, S. R., and Behre, J. A., *J. Biol. Chem.* **114:** 515 (1936).
4. Langley, W. D., and Evans, M., *J. Biol. Chem.* **115:** 333 (1936).
5. Clark, L. C., Jr., and Thompson, H. L., *Anal. Chem.* **21:** 1218 (1949).
6. Jansen, A. P., Sombroeck, W., and Noyons, E. C., *Chem. Weekblad* **43:** 731 (1947).
7. Kingsley, G. R., and Schaffert, R. R., Unpublished data from Clinical Biochemistry Laboratory of Veterans Administration Center, Los Angeles.

Glucose

Submitted by: NELSON F. YOUNG, Department of Clinical Pathology and Hospital Laboratories, Medical College of Virginia, Richmond, Virginia.

Checked by: ALBERT E. SOBEL, Jewish Hospital of Brooklyn, Brooklyn, New York.

Author: O. FOLIN and H. WU, *J. Biol. Chem.* **41:** 367 (1920).

Introduction

Probably no commonly determined substance is estimated by such a wide variety of methods as is blood sugar. Although the Folin-Wu method here described is by no means the most economical, the most convenient, the easiest, the most specific, or the most reproducible, it is one which is still widely used in clinical laboratories throughout the world. For this reason no apology is necessary for presenting it in a book of methods such as this, with a re-evaluation of it in the light of modern instrumentation and current medical needs.

The greatest single objection to the method is the inclusion of 15–30 mg. % of non-glucose "saccharoid" when performed on the commonly used tungstic acid filtrate. This discrepancy between the "true blood glucose" obtained by fermentation procedures and approached by several copper reduction procedures and the Folin-Wu method is serious enough to discourage its use by many laboratories. However, the fact that the method is still widely used attests its usefulness as an aid in diagnosis and therapy in many instances.

Principle

When glucose or other reducing sugar is heated in alkaline solution with cupric ion, the sugar and its various decomposition products reduce the copper, with the result that insoluble Cu_2O is formed. This is not a stoichiometric reaction, and, depending on conditions of temperature, duration of heating, degree of alkalinity, etc., the ratio of glucose to Cu_2O formed may be varied over a wide range. For any given set of conditions, however, the amount of Cu_2O

will depend to a large extent on the amount of sugar present. After the heating period, the Cu_2O is estimated by allowing it to reduce phosphomolybdic acid with a proportionate formation of molybdenum blue which is determined colorimetrically.

Reagents

1. *Alkaline copper reagent:* Dissolve 40.0 g. of anhydrous reagent grade sodium carbonate in about 400 ml. of distilled water, and transfer to a 1-l. volumetric flask. Then add 7.5 g. of tartaric acid, and 4.5 g. of $CuSO_4 \cdot 5H_2O$. Mix and dilute to 1 l. With reagent grade chemicals this solution may be used immediately, and it is stable indefinitely. Should a small amount of cuprous oxide form, filter it out before using as it will increase the blank reading.

2. *Phosphomolybdic acid solution:* To 70 g. of molybdic acid and 10 g. of sodium tungstate add 400 ml. of 10% sodium hydroxide and 400 ml. of water. Boil for 20–40 minutes to remove ammonia. Cool and dilute to about 700 ml. Add 250 ml. of sirupy orthophosphoric acid (85% H_3PO_4) and dilute to 1 l.

3. *Standard glucose solution:* The glucose stock solution is prepared by weighing 10.000 g. of anhydrous glucose which is then diluted to 1 l. with 0.2% benzoic acid solution. Working standards containing 0.2 and 0.4 mg. per 2 ml. are made fresh daily by diluting the stock solution 1:100 and 2:100 with water. Pure glucose may be obtained from the National Bureau of Standards; Merck's anhydrous highest purity glucose is also satisfactory.

Procedure

Add 2 ml. of 1:10 blood, serum, or plasma filtrate (see Discussion) to a Folin-Wu sugar tube, and to three similar tubes add 2 ml. of water and 2 ml. of standard sugar solution containing 0.2 and 0.40 mg. of glucose, respectively. To each tube add 2 ml. of alkaline copper solution and mix. The surface of the mixture must now have reached the constricted portion of the tube. Immerse the tubes at least 4 inches in briskly boiling water, and heat for exactly 8 minutes. Remove and cool the tubes in cold water without undue shaking. To each tube add 2 ml. of phosphomolybdic acid reagent, and mix. Dilute to 25 ml. with water and mix by inversion.

For colorimetric comparison the blank tube containing no glucose is omitted, and the unknowns are compared with the standard most nearly matching them.

Calculation:

$$\frac{R_s}{R_u} \times \text{mg. glucose in standard} \times \frac{100}{0.2} = \text{Mg. \% glucose}$$

See Comments for deviation from the Beer-Lambert law.

For photometric measurement, a 420-mμ wavelength seems most satisfactory for measurement. In a 1-cm. cell, satisfactory readings are obtained up to about 400 mg. %. The calculation with the blank adjusted to zero optical density is:

$$\frac{O D_u}{O D_s} \times \text{mg. glucose in standard} \times \frac{100}{0.2} = \text{Mg. \% glucose}$$

Comments

The problem of saccharoid interference can be attacked in two ways. The interfering substances may be eliminated from the filtrate as in the Somogyi (1) zinc filtrate. These filtrates are not suitable for use in determining many other substances, however, and hence it is necessary to make two different filtrates for a specimen on which, for example, a blood sugar and a non-protein nitrogen are desired. Most laboratories find such duplication undesirable. The Folin-Wu method does give values approaching the true glucose content when applied to Somogyi filtrates.

The second approach to the problem is to devise a copper reagent which will react specifically with glucose. In seeking such a reagent, numerous modifications of the Folin-Wu method have been proposed which to some extent improve results. None of the modification equal the specificity of the Benedict method and its various modifications, however (2, 3).

The amount of cuprous oxide formed by increasing amounts of sugar does not increase strictly proportionately except over relatively narrow ranges for any given set of conditions. In addition, cuprous copper tends to reoxidize when exposed to air in hot suspension. A third problem with regard to measurement lies in the tendency of molybdenum blue to fade unless special precautions are taken.

These three difficulties all tend to cause deviations from strict linearity in the relationship between glucose present and blue color observed, but they are, or may be, minimized by the following means.

For visual colorimetry the tables prepared by Oser and Karr (4) may be used to correct for overall non-linearity. For photoelectric work the best linearity is obtained by using a wavelength of 420 mμ (5). The deviation from the Beer-Lambert law will depend on the particular photometer used, but good results are obtained in the range 40–400 mg. %. For lower sugar values than this, additional standards of 0.04 and 0.08 mg. of glucose may be used, and samples with a content higher than about 400 mg. % should be appropriately diluted and rerun. The shape of the Folin-Wu tube and the avoidance of shaking while the tubes are hot minimize the reoxidation of copper. Stabilization of the molybdenum blue may be accomplished by heating the tubes for a period of 2 minutes after the addition of the phosphomolybdate reagent.

The following data were obtained using the method exactly as described. Folin-Wu filtrates (6) were used, and the developed color was estimated on either a Coleman junior spectrophotometer using 0.75-cm. I.D., round Pyrex test tubes matched for optical uniformity, or on a Klett-Summerson photoelectric colorimeter using standard Klett tubes.

Fasting blood sugars were run in duplicate on ninety hospitalized patients who were selected as being free of liver, pancreatic, adrenal, or other hormonal dysfunction. In no case did the duplicates fail to check within 4 mg. %. The extreme variation was from 72 to 132 mg. % with 91% of the values falling between 90 and 115 mg. %. The average blood sugar was found to be 103.4 mg. %.

Recovery of glucose from eighteen blood samples containing from 80 to 570 mg. % of reducing substance was found to average 99.0%, with a variation of 97.5–102%. Variations in color from day to day in the standard tubes were as much as 8%. Careful control of heating time and temperature failed to disclose the reason for this, and it is strongly recommended, therefore, that no determinations be made without the inclusion of standard controls.

BIBLIOGRAPHY

1. Somogyi, M., *J. Biol. Chem.* **86:** 655 (1939).
2. Benedict, S. R., *J. Biol. Chem.* **92:** 141 (1931).
3. Sunderman, W., and Fuller, *Am. J. Clin. Path.* **21:** 1077 (1951).
4. Oser, B., and Karr, W. G., *J. Biol. Chem.* **67:** 319 (1926).
5. Hawk, P. B., Oser, B. L., and Summerson, W. H., *Practical Physiological Chemistry*, 12th ed., p. 522, Blakiston Company, Philadelphia.
6. Folin, O., and Wu, H., *J. Biol. Chem.* **38:** 81 (1919).

Glucose

Submitted by: JOHN G. REINHOLD, Pepper Laboratory of Clinical Medicine, Hospital of the University of Pennsylvania, Philadelphia, Pennsylvania.

Checked by: MARGARET VANDERAU, Presbyterian Hospital, Philadelphia, Pennsylvania.

PHILIP E. HALPERN, Jewish Hospital, Philadelphia, Pennsylvania.

Author: N. NELSON, *J. Biol. Chem.* **153**: 375 (1944).

M. SOMOGYI, *J. Biol. Chem.* **160**: 62 (1945).

A. Reagents for Precipitation of Proteins

1. 5% zinc sulfate: Dissolve 100 g. of $ZnSO_4 \cdot 7H_2O$ in water, and dilute to 2000 ml. in a graduated cylinder.

2. 0.3 N barium hydroxide: Dissolve 90 g. of $Ba(OH)_2 \cdot 8H_2O$ in water, and dilute to 2000 ml. in a graduated cylinder. Filter if cloudy. Store in well-stoppered containers filled to capacity.

Concentrations of the working solutions of Zn and Ba are not as important as the fact that they exactly neutralize one another. To titrate, measure 10 ml. of $ZnSO_4$ solution into a 250-ml. flask, and add approximately 50 ml. of H_2O and 4 drops of phenolphthalein indicator. Slowly titrate with $Ba(OH)_2$, using continual agitation. (*Note:* Too rapid addition of the $Ba(OH)_2$ will give a false end point.) The titration is carried out until 1 drop of $Ba(OH)_2$ turns the solution a faint pink. The result should be such that 10 ml. of $ZnSO_4$ require 10 ml. of $Ba(OH)_2 \pm 0.05$ ml. If one or the other of the two solutions is too strong, add distilled water in appropriate quantities, and repeat the titration. Store the solutions in aspirator bottles. That containing the barium hydroxide should carry a soda-lime tube in the stopper. The solutions should be tested in advance by preparing a trial filtrate from blood. Filtration should proceed rapidly to give a clear filtrate with little tendency to foam. If faults are noted, repeat the titration, and adjust solutions accordingly.

B. Reagents for Determination of Glucose

COPPER REAGENT, SOLUTION A: Dissolve 50 g. of Na_2CO_3 (anhydrous), 50 g. of Rochelle salt, 40 g. of $NaHCO_3$, and 400 g. of Na_2SO_4 (anhydrous) in about 1600 ml. of water, and dilute to 2 l. Filter if necessary. This solution should be stored where the temperature will not fall below 20° C. A sediment may form after a few days. This may be filtered off without detriment to the reagent.

COPPER REAGENT, SOLUTION B: Dissolve 150 g. of $CuSO_4 \cdot 5H_2O$ in 1 l. of water. Add 0.5 ml. of conc. H_2SO_4.

3. Alkaline copper reagent: Prepare on the day it is to be used by measuring 4 ml. of solution B into a 100-ml. mixing cylinder and diluting to 100 ml. with solution A. Mix well.

4. Arsenomolybdate color reagent: Dissolve 100 g. of ammonium molybdate in 1800 ml. of distilled water. Add 84 ml. of concentrated sulfuric acid and mix. Add 12 g. of disodium orthoarsenate ($Na_2HAsO_4 \cdot 7H_2O$) dissolved in 100 ml. of water. Mix, and place in an incubator for 24–48 hours at 37° C. (An alternative, although less desirable, method is to heat to 55° C. for about 25 minutes while stirring actively.) Decomposition of the reagent is characterized by precipitation of a bright yellow compound. Prepared by the first method it is stable indefinitely when stored in a glass-stoppered brown bottle.

5. Stock standard glucose solution: Weigh 1.000 g. of purest dextrose (obtainable from National Bureau of Standards). Transfer to a 100-ml. volumetric flask, and dilute to the mark with 0.2% benzoic acid solution; 1 ml. contains 10 mg. of glucose.

50-MG. STANDARD (I): Dilute 0.5 ml. of stock solution to 200 ml. in a volumetric flask with 0.2% benzoic acid solution; 0.5 ml. contains 0.0125 mg. of glucose.

100-MG. STANDARD (II): Dilute 1 ml. of stock solution to 200 ml.; 0.5 ml. contains 0.025 mg. of glucose.

200-MG. STANDARD (III): Dilute 2 ml. of stock solution to 200 ml.; 0.5 ml. contains 0.05 mg. of glucose. Standards diluted with benzoic acid keep indefinitely at room temperature.

6. Benzoic acid solution, 0.2%: Place approximately 4 g. of benzoic acid in a 3-l. Pyrex flask. Add 2 l. of water. Heat to boiling, but do not boil.

Procedure

1. Preparation of protein-free filtrate for blood sugar and urea N:
Measure 1 ml. of blood into a 50-ml. flask. If urea is to be done, add
2 drops of urease. Mix well and let stand 30 minutes, shaking occasionally. If only sugar is needed, proceed at once with the next
step without addition of urease. Add 9.5 ml. of barium hydroxide
while rotating flask. Add 9.5 ml. of zinc sulfate solution while
mixing. Shake vigorously. Filter through Whatman No. 1 paper
or equivalent.

2. Method: The test is made in a test tube approximately 15 × 125
mm. If the Klett-Summerson photometer is used, the test is carried out in the calibrated graduated cuvettes.

Measure into the tube 0.5 ml. of barium-zinc filtrate and add 1
ml. of alkaline copper reagent. Mix each tube by tapping. Place
a marble on top and heat in a vigorously boiling water bath 20
minutes, or place in a pressure cooker (see Remarks) for 5 minutes
at 115° C. Place tubes in water at room temperature for 1 minute.
Add 1 ml. of arsenomolybdate reagent, and mix. Dilute to the 10-
ml. mark with water. Mix by inverting. Measure the absorbance
at 540 mμ by means of a photocolorimeter, by the conventional
procedure using the blank for setting the zero, or by the simplified
method (see below).

3. Standard: Use 0.5 ml. of each of the three standards, and proceed as described above for filtrates. For ordinary purposes, one
standard will suffice.

4. Blank: Substitute water for filtrate.

Calculation

1. Conventional method: R is the reading of the unknown, and S
is the reading of the standard.

Using standard I (0.0125 mg. of glucose): Glucose, mg. per 100

$$ml. = R \times \frac{50}{S}.$$

Using standard II (0.025 mg. of glucose): Glucose, mg. per 100

$$ml. = R \times \frac{100}{S}.$$

Using standard III (0.05 mg. of glucose): Glucose, mg. per 100 ml. $= R \times \dfrac{200}{S}$.

2. Direct reading method: For use with photometers having scales measuring absorbance, with the 540-mμ filter in place.

Place the blank in the photocolorimeter and make the zero setting. Read the standards. Note whether the 50-mg. standard reads approximately 50 scale divisions, or some convenient fraction thereof; the 100-mg. standard reads 100, etc. Then place the standard reading nearest to the unknown in the instrument, set the dial, if necessary, to the figure representing the glucose equivalent of the standard, and adjust the shutter to give a null reading. The scale reading will represent blood sugar or a simple fraction thereof. If the standards do not agree within 5% of the expected readings, use the conventional method or substitute a filter of another wavelength. The concentration/absorbance relationship may be adjusted by introducing other filters in place of the 540-mμ filter. When the required correspondence is found proceed as above.

Microtechnique

Draw cutaneous blood into a 0.1-ml. pipette and expel it into a centrifuge tube containing 0.95 ml. of Ba(OH)$_2$ solution. Rinse the pipette two or three times by drawing up and expelling the solution into the centrifuge tube. Add 0.95 ml. of ZnSO$_4$ solution, and mix the contents of the tube thoroughly by tapping. Allow the tubes to stand for 3–5 minutes, and centrifuge for 5 minutes.

After centrifuging, pipette 0.5 ml. of the supernatant fluid into a tube and carry out the analysis as described in the procedure for larger blood samples.

Blank: Substitute 0.5 ml. of water for the filtrate or standard.

Standards: Same as in the macro method: 0.5 ml. of each of the 50-, 100-, and 200-mg. standards.

Photometer readings: Use blank for zero settings for the standards and unknowns. Results may be obtained either by direct photometry or by the conventional method.

Calculation: Same as in the standard method.

Comments

Inclusion of sodium sulfate in the copper reagent inhibits reoxidation of cuprous oxide and makes unnecessary the use of constricted tubes for preventing reoxidation. It is possible, therefore, to carry out the procedure directly in a cuvette of the test tube type. The arsenomolybdate reagent gives stable colors that remain unchanged for more than 24 hours.

In the method as originally described, heating was continued for 20 minutes in a boiling water bath. The use of a small autoclave (household pressure cooker) reduces this time to 5 minutes. In our experience 2.5 minutes is required to heat the pressure cooker to 115° C. (15 lb. pressure). Holding it 2.5 minutes at this temperature suffices.

Barium zinc precipitation of proteins removes the non-sugar reducing substances effectively. The method thus gives "true" glucose values.

Obviously a precise result cannot be obtained beyond the usual limits of sensitivity of the photometer, although the method itself maintains rectilinear proportionality between absorbance and glucose concentrations far beyond these instrumental limits. If readings exceed 350 mg. per 100 ml. (the upper limit that can be safely measured with a Klett-Summerson photometer), the glucose concentration can be approximated by diluting with arsenomolybdate reagent diluted 1:10 with water. It is our practice, however, to repeat the test, using 0.1 ml. of filtrate. The final reading then is multiplied by 5. For precise measurement of very low blood glucose concentration, addition of 0.5 ml. of standard I is recommended.

Oxalate or fluoride ions do not interfere when present in low concentrations. Excessive quantities are likely to cause difficulty in preparation of filtrates.

In our experience the precision of this method is superior to that of the Folin-Wu method and its several modifications, the Benedict method, and the various ferricyanide reduction methods. Somogyi (1) recently described a modified reagent containing less copper and giving lower blanks.

Application

The importance of blood glucose determinations is so well known that little comment is required. The most important application is the detection of diabetes mellitus and, subsequently, the control of this disease by evaluation of the effect of various dosages of insulin and varying compositions of diet on blood sugar.

Most clinicians agree that blood glucose determinations are more informative when done while the patient is in the fasting state. However, many individuals suffering from diabetes mellitus of mild character do not have an elevated fasting blood glucose, and it may be helpful to analyze blood collected 1 or 2 hours after a meal. Glucose tolerance tests provide a more rigorous diagnostic test in these circumstances.

The detection of low blood glucose concentrations is another important function of blood glucose determinations. Commonly, hypoglycemia is caused by overdosage with insulin. Diseases characterized by hypoglycemia are uncommon; nevertheless, an appreciable number of individuals are so afflicted. Hypersecretion of insulin is the most frequent cause. Endocrine imbalance resulting in diminished secretion of hormone antagonists of insulin as in adrenocortical or anterior pituitary insufficiency is another cause of lowered blood glucose. Depletion of glycogen stores of the liver by starvation or liver disease may cause hypoglycemia. Poorly balanced diets containing carbohydrate almost exclusively may be a cause of low blood glucose. A similar effect has been noted as a result of diets very rich in fat and poor in carbohydrate.

Numerous causes for elevated blood glucose exist besides diabetes mellitus. Hypoxia due to many causes, traumatic injury to the brain, especially if associated with hemorrhage, febrile illness, liver disease at certain stages, hypersecretion of thyroid, anterior pituitary, and adrenal glands, and far advanced renal disease commonly are characterized by hyperglycemia.

Normal Values

Blood glucose of healthy subjects measured 12–16 hours after a meal averages 85 mg. per 100 ml. Ninety-five per cent of the values will range between 65 and 110 mg. per 100 ml. Healthy elderly subjects show somewhat higher values. Normal values are the same for children as for adults.

In the fasting individual capillary or arterial blood and venous blood glucose concentrations are the same or so nearly so as to be interchangeable for practical purposes. After ingestion of glucose or food, concentrations in capillary blood are higher.

BIBLIOGRAPHY

1. Somogyi, M., *J. Biol. Chem.* **195**: 19 (1952).

Lipase (Tributyrinase)

Submitted by: CARL ALPER, Division of Biological Chemistry, Hahnemann Medical College and Hospital of Philadelphia, Pennsylvania.

Checked by: LT. M. E. HODES and LT. (J.G.) B. GARLAND, U. S. Naval Medical School, Department of Physiological Chemistry, National Naval Medical Center, Bethesda, Maryland.

Authors: N. P. GOLDSTEIN, J. EPSTEIN, and J. H. ROE, *J. Lab. Clin. Med.* **33:** 1047 (1948).

Introduction

The complex of enzymes known as lipases or esterases catalyzes the hydrolysis of simple esters or glycerides. The fatty acids liberated are quantitatively determined by titration with standard alkali. Lipolytic activity of serum is determined by the quantity of fatty acids set free from an emulsion of tributyrin in 1 hour by 1 ml of serum. The units of activity are expressed in milliliters of 0.1 N alkali required to titrate free butyric acid.

Reagents

1. Calcium acetate solution, 2%.

2. Sodium diethyl barbiturate solution, 0.5%.

3. Sodium choleate solution, 667.5 mg. per 100 ml.: This reagent may be omitted without interfering with the results.

4. Tween 20 (Atlas Powder Co.).

5. Methocel (Dow Chemical Co.): 15 centipoises viscosity.

6. Tributyrin, c.p.: If necessary, purify as follows: neutralize the fatty acids with sodium bicarbonate, wash with distilled water, distill under reduced pressure.

7. Tributyrin emulsion: Add 250 ml. of 2% calcium acetate solution to 250 ml. of 0.5% sodium diethyl barbiturate solution. Add to the solution 1 ml. of sodium choleate solution, 0.25 ml. of Tween 20, and 0.5 g. of Methocel. Finally, add 6.25 ml. of tributyrin, and. mix in a Waring Blendor for 3–5 minutes. Adjust to pH 8.55. The emulsion is stable with respect to fat globule size and auto-lipolysis for at least 14 days when kept under refrigeration (5–10° C). If stored at room temperature for 14 days, the pH of the buffered emulsion falls to about 7.7.

8. Ethanol-ether solution: Add 100 ml. of diethyl ether to 900 ml. of 95% ethanol. Mix thoroughly.

9. Standard alkali solution: Either sodium hydroxide or potassium hydroxide may be used. Prepare 0.05 N solution.

Procedure

Add 20 ml. of buffered tributyrin emulsion to each of two 150-ml. flasks. One is the *test* flask; the other is the *control* flask. Add 1 ml. of serum to the *test* flask, and mix well. Incubate the *test* flask for 1 hour at 37° C. Add 50 ml. of ethanol-ether solution to each flask, and mix well. Add 1 ml. of serum to the *control* flask. Titrate each flask to pH 10.65 (pH meter) with 0.05 N alkali, using a microburette. Stir vigorously during titration. Record the volume of standard alkali used. (For titration with colorimetric indicator, use phenolphthalein.) It is suggested that the determination be carried out in duplicate.

Calculation

1. Volume of standard alkali used in titration of the test flask minus the volume of standard alkali used in titration of the control is equal to the volume of standard alkali equivalent to fatty acids released by lipolytic activity of serum.

2. (Volume of standard alkali determined in 1) $\times$

$$\frac{normality\ of\ alkali}{0.1} = \text{Units of tributyrinase activity (ml. 0.1 } N \text{ alkali)}.$$

Comments

1. Method: This procedure overcomes certain technical difficulties which have previously made lipase activity determinations difficult (1, 2, 3).

(a) Recent studies (4) indicate that the difference in activity of serum for triolein and tributyrin may be related to the substrate specificity of the enzyme.

(b) The determination of lipolytic activity in approximately 2 hours affords economy of time.

(c) This emulsion is constant in its composition over a long period of time, as determined by measurements of fat globule size and surface tension (5, 6, 7).

(d) Electrometric determination of the end point of titration reduces to a minimum errors associated with titration in a heterogeneous medium.

2. *Significance:* Elevated values of serum lipase activity are indicative of acute pancreatic disease in contrast to the usual normal levels found in chronic disease of the pancreas. Increase in serum lipase has also been reported in about 40% of cases of carcinoma of pancreas, in about 60% of cases of carcinoma of ampulla of Vater, and in about 10% of cases of chronic biliary tract disease. Occasionally, elevated values of serum lipase are observed in cirrhosis of the liver, hepatitis, duodenal ulcer, and conditions associated with secondary pancreatic involvement.

Reduced values of serum lipase activity are associated with deficiencies in pancreatic and liver function and starvation.

Normal Range

1. American Red Cross (Philadelphia), 100 blood donors:

Total range	0.76–1.61
Range of 65% of results	1.01–1.40
Average	1.20 ± 0.20

2. Hahnemann Medical College (Philadelphia), 35 volunteers, medical students, age 21–25 years.

Total range	0.73–1.39
Range of 73% of results	1.00–1.39
Average	1.09–

3. Naval Medical Center (Bethesda, Maryland), 43 normal subjects:

Total range	0.89–2.10
Range of 75% of results	1.00–1.45
Average	1.29–

BIBLIOGRAPHY

1. Cherry, I. S., and Crandall, L. A. Jr., *Am. J. Physiol.* **100:** 266 (1932).
2. Comfort, M. W., and Osterberg, A. E., *Med. Clin. N. Amer.* **24:** 1137 (1940).
3. Shwachman, H., Farber, S., and Maddock, C. L., *Am. J. Diseases Children* **66:** 418 (1943).

4. Alper, C., and Polakoff, P. P., Jr., and Alexander, E. *Federation Proc.* 12: 167 (1953).
5. Alper, C., *Clin. Chem.* 4: 14 (1952).
6. Alper, C., and Polakoff, P. P., Jr., *Federation Proc.* 10: 155 (1951).
7. Alper, C., and Polakoff, P. P., Jr., *Federation Proc.* 11: 180 (1952).

Alkaline and Acid Phosphatase

Submitted by: JULIUS J. CARR, The Mount Sinai Hospital, New York, New York.

Checked by: MIRIAM REINER, Gallinger Municipal Hospital, Washington, D. C.

Authors: E. J. KING and A. R. ARMSTRONG, *Can. Med. Assoc. J.* **31**: 376 (1934).

Principle of the Method

The estimation of alkaline or acid phosphatase activity depends upon measurement of the amount of hydrolysis which takes place when the enzyme is allowed to act upon disodium phenyl phosphate at a selected pH at 37° C. Equivalent amounts of phenol and phosphate are liberated. After hydrolysis, protein is precipitated with the reagent of Folin and Ciocalteu (1), and phenol is determined by measuring the blue color which is produced by the addition of sodium carbonate. The color is probably due to the formation of "heteropoly blue" complexes which result upon treatment of phosphotungstate and phosphomolybdate with reducing agents, phenol in this instance.

A *unit* of *alkaline phosphatase* is defined as the amount of enzyme which will liberate 1 mg. of phenol from a 0.005 M solution of disodium phenyl phosphate during *15 minutes* at 37° C. in carbonate-bicarbonate buffer at pH 10. The corresponding *unit* of *acid phosphatase* represents the amount of enzyme which will liberate 1 mg. of phenol from a 0.005 M solution of disodium phenyl phosphate during *1 hour* at 37° C. in citrate buffer at pH 4.9.

Allowing for dilution by the added serum, the actual concentration of substrate is 4.76 mM (0.00476 M).

Reagents

1. Stock phenol reagent (1): Dissolve 100 g. of sodium tungstate ($Na_2WO_4 \cdot 2H_2O$) and 25 g. of sodium molybdate ($Na_2MoO_4.2H_2O$) in 700 ml. of water in a 1500-ml. round-bottomed flask. Add 50 ml. of 85% phosphoric acid and 100 ml. of concentrated hydrochloric acid. Mix thoroughly. Fit a reflux condenser to the flask by means of a rubber stopper or cork wrapped in tin foil, or, preferably, use standard-taper all-glass joints. Boil the solution gently for 10 hours. Remove the condenser, add 150 g. of lithium sulfate (Li_2SO_4), and wash down with 50 ml. of water. After solution is complete, add 5–10 drops of liquid bromine, and boil for 15 minutes to remove the excess bromine. The solution should be clear and golden-yellow in appearance. If it shows a greenish tint, repeat the treatment with bromine. Cool the solution to room temperature, dilute to 1 l., and filter if necessary through glass wool into a glass-stoppered brown bottle. This reagent is stable for several months.

2. Dilute phenol reagent: Dilute 1 vol. of stock phenol reagent with 2 vol. of distilled water. This solution is reasonably stable when stored in a dark-brown bottle. Discard when a greenish tint becomes noticeable.

3. Substrate: 0.01 *M* disodium phenyl phosphate (2). Dissolve 2.18 g. of reagent grade disodium monophenyl phosphate in 1 l. of distilled water. Sterilize the solution by bringing it quickly to the boiling point. Then cool it immediately, add a few drops of chloroform, and store in the refrigerator.

4. Alkaline buffer: 0.06 *M* Na_2CO_3, 0.04 *M* $NaHCO_3$ (2). Dissolve 6.36 g. of anhydrous sodium carbonate and 3.36 g. of sodium bicarbonate in approximately 500 ml. of distilled water contained in a 1-l. volumetric flask. Dilute to mark, and mix. Store in a refrigerator. The pH of this solution should be 10.0.

5. Acid buffer: 0.176 *M* disodium citrate, 0.024 *M* monosodium citrate (3). Dissolve 21.0 g. of reagent grade citric acid monohydrate, crystalline, in 200 ml. of distilled water, contained in a 500-ml. volumetric flask. Add 188 ml. of standardized 1 *N* sodium hydroxide, and dilute to volume. The pH of this solution should be 4.9. Check potentiometrically, and adjust if necessary by the addition of either 0.1 *N* sodium hydroxide or 0.1 *N* hydrochloric acid. Add a few drops of chloroform, and store in the refrigerator.

6. Buffered alkaline substrate: Mix 500 ml. of substrate (solution 3) with 500 ml. of alkaline buffer (solution 4). Store in refrigerator.

7. Buffered acid substrate: Mix 250 ml. of substrate (solution 3) with 250 ml. of acid buffer (solution 5). Store in refrigerator.

8. Sodium carbonate, 6% solution (w/v): Dissolve 60 g. of anhydrous sodium carbonate in distilled water, and dilute to 1 l. Store in a Pyrex or paraffin-lined bottle.

9. Sodium carbonate, 8% solution (w/v): Dissolve 40 g. of anhydrous sodium carbonate in distilled water, and dilute to 500 ml. Store in a Pyrex or paraffin-lined bottle.

10. *Phenol stock standard, 1 mg./ml.:* Transfer approximately 1.2 g. of reagent grade crystalline phenol to a 1-l. volumetric flask, and dissolve in approximately 200 ml. of 0.1 N hydrochloric acid (prepared by diluting 8.5 ml. of concentrated acid to 1 l. with distilled water). Dilute to volume with 0.1 N hydrochloric acid.

STANDARDIZATION: 0.1 N solutions of sodium thiosulfate (25.0 g. of $Na_2S_2O_3 \cdot 5H_2O$ per liter) and of iodine (prepared by diluting a solution containing 25 g. of pure KI, 25 ml. of water, and 12.7 g. of resublimed iodine to 1 l.) are standardized by titration. The 0.1 N solution of potassium biiodate (3.250 g. of reagent grade $KH(IO_3)_2$ per liter) is used to standardize the 0.1 N thiosulfate. Then the thiosulfate is used to standardize the 0.1 N iodine solution.

Immediately prior to titration of biiodate with thiosulfate, iodine is liberated from the standard solution by transferring 25 ml. to a solution prepared by adding 5 ml. of 6 N hydrochloric acid to a solution of 2 g. of pure potassium iodide in 3 ml. of water.

To standardize the phenol stock solution, accurately transfer 25 ml. of the solution to a 250-ml. glass-stoppered Erlenmeyer flask, add 50 ml. of 0.1 N sodium hydroxide solution (4.0 g./l.), and heat to 65° C. Add 25 ml. of 0.1 N iodine, and mix. Stopper the flask, and allow to stand at room temperature for 45 minutes. Add 5 ml. of concentrated hydrochloric acid, and titrate the excess iodine with 0.1 N sodium thiosulfate, using 1 ml. of 1% starch as indicator.

CALCULATION: Mg. phenol per 25 ml. = 1.568 × (ml. 0.1 N I_2 − ml. 0.1 N $Na_2S_2O_3$ used). If more than 25 mg. of phenol is found in 25 ml., adjust to this concentration by suitable dilution with 0.1 N hydrochloric acid. This solution keeps indefinitely at refrigerator temperature.

11. *Dilute phenol standard, 0.05 mg./ml.:* Transfer 5 ml. of the phenol stock standard to a 100-ml. volumetric flask, and dilute to volume with distilled water. Store in refrigerator. This solution may be kept one month.

Procedure

1. Alkaline phosphatase

(a) INCUBATION AND DEPROTEINIZATION: Transfer 4 ml. of buffered alkaline substrate (solution 6) to each of two test tubes (5

× ⅝-in., bacteriological weight, are suitable) labeled A and B, and allow the solutions to warm for 3 minutes in a water bath regulated at 37° C.   Add 0.2 ml. of serum (or plasma) to tube A, mix at once, and allow both tubes to remain in the water bath.   Exactly 15 minutes after the addition of serum to tube A, pipette 2 ml. of dilute phenol reagent (solution 2) into each tube, and mix well.   Add 0.2 ml. of serum to tube B, mix again, and centrifuge both tubes.

(b) PREPARATION OF STANDARD: Measure 1 ml. of dilute phenol standard (solution 11) into a test tube.   Add 3.2 ml. of distilled water and 2 ml. of dilute phenol reagent, and mix.

(c) PREPARATION OF REAGENT BLANK: To a tube containing 4.2 ml. of distilled water add 2 ml. of dilute phenol reagent, and mix.

(d) DEVELOPMENT AND MEASUREMENT OF COLOR: Add 2 ml. of clear supernatant solution, 2 ml. of prepared standard, and 2 ml. of reagent blank to appropriately labeled tubes.   To each tube add 8 ml. of 6% sodium carbonate (solution 8), mix well, and allow to stand 20 minutes for complete color development.

Measure the resulting blue colors in a suitable photometer, such as the Coleman spectrophotometer or the Klett photoelectric colorimeter at 660 mμ (red).   With instruments calibrated in terms of absorbance (optical density) pour the reagent blank into a suitable cuvette (e.g., Coleman No. 6-302), and adjust absorbance reading to zero against this solution.   Record readings of the standard and of solutions A and B.   Subtract reading of solution B from that of solution A.

CALCULATION:

$$\text{K.A.U. per 100 ml.} = 0.0161 \times \frac{R_A - R_B}{R_S} \times \frac{6.2}{2.0} \times \frac{100}{0.2}$$

$$\text{K.A.U. per 100 ml.} = 25.0 \times \frac{R_A - R_B}{R_S}$$

Where K.A.U. = alkaline phosphatase expressed as King-Armstrong Units.
0.0161 = milligrams of phenol in final standard solution.
R_A = absorbance reading of solution A.
R_B = absorbance reading of solution B.
R_S = reading of phenol standard.

6.2 = combined volume of serum plus buffered substrate plus dilute phenol reagent.
2.0 = aliquot portion of this solution taken for color
   development.
0.2 = volume of serum taken for analysis.

2. Acid phosphatase

(a) INCUBATION AND DEPROTEINIZATION: Transfer 4 ml. of buffered acid substrate (solution 7) to each of two test tubes, labeled
C and D, and warm the solutions for 3 minutes in a water bath at
37° C.   Add 0.2 ml. of unhemolyzed serum or plasma to tube C,
mix at once, and allow both tubes to remain in the water bath.
Exactly 1 hour after the addition of serum to tube C, pipette 2 ml.
of dilute phenol reagent (solution 2) into each tube, and mix well.
Add 0.2 ml. of serum to tube D, mix again, and centrifuge both tubes.

(b) PREPARATION OF TREATED STANDARD (STANDARD PLUS PHENOL
REAGENT): Measure 1 ml. of dilute phenol standard (solution 11)
into a test tube.   Add 3.2 ml. of distilled water and 2 ml. of dilute
phenol reagent, and mix.

(c) PREPARATION OF REAGENT BLANK: To a tube containing 4.2
ml. of distilled water add 2 ml. of dilute phenol reagent, and mix.
(When both alkaline and acid phosphatase are to be determined,
only one standard and reagent blank need be prepared.)

(d) DEVELOPMENT AND MEASUREMENT OF COLOR: Add 4 ml. of
each clear supernatant solution, prepared standard, and reagent
blank to an appropriately labeled tube.   To each solution add 6 ml.
of 8% sodium carbonate (solution 9), mix well, and allow to stand
for 20 minutes.

Pour the reagent blank into a suitable cuvette (e.g., Coleman No.
6-302), and set the indicator of the photometer to zero absorbance
against this solution at 660 mμ (red).   Record absorbance readings
of the standard and of solutions C and D.   Subtract reading of
solution D from that of solution C.

CALCULATION:

$$\text{K.A.U. per 100 ml.} = 0.0322 \times \frac{R_C - R_D}{R_s} \times \frac{6.2}{4.0} \times \frac{100}{0.2}$$

$$\text{K.A.U. per 100 ml.} = 25.0 \times \frac{R_C - R_D}{R_s}$$

Where K.A.U. = acid phosphatase expressed as King-Armstrong Units.

0.0322 = milligrams of phenol in final standard solution.

R_C = absorbance reading of solution C.

R_D = absorbance reading of solution D.

R_s = reading of phenol standard.

6.2 = combined volume of serum plus buffered substrate plus dilute phenol reagent.

4.0 = aliquot portion of this solution taken for color development.

0.2 = volume of serum taken for analysis.

Comments

Blood serum (or plasma) is known to contain at least two enzymes which are able to catalyze the hydrolysis of phosphate esters of alcohols such as glycerol, phenol, p-nitrophenol, and phenolphthalein. These phosphatases may be differentiated by the pH at which each exhibits its maximum activity.

Elevated values for serum alkaline phosphatase (optimum pH 9–10) are usually found in cases of disordered bone metabolism as well as in hepatic and in biliary tract disease. Markedly increased values are found in cases of active rickets, in hyperparathyroidism, and usually in Paget's disease. Slightly elevated values are occasionally found in patients with generalized osteoporosis, marked hyperthyroidism, osteomalacia, metastatic carcinoma involving bone, healing fractures, "marble bones," and Gaucher's disease with bone resorption (4).

Since alkaline phosphatase values tend to parallel the rate of active bone formation, higher normal values are found in children than in adults. Phosphatase levels are low at birth, rise rapidly to a maximum during the first month of life, and remain fairly stable during the second year. The values in later childhood fall within the normal adult range.

When elevated serum bilirubin levels are found, the determination of alkaline phosphatase activity is often utilized in differential diagnosis. Normal alkaline phosphatase values are found in hemolytic jaundice, while elevated values indicate hepatocellular damage or biliary obstruction. Although markedly increased values are associated with biliary obstruction more often than with hepatic disease, considerable overlapping of results have been reported. Thus, an unequivocal diagnosis is often difficult without the aid of other tests of liver function.

Elevated serum acid phosphatase values have been found almost exclusively in cases of carcinoma of the prostate with metastases. Values above 4 units have been obtained in about 85% of these cases. Slight increases (maximum 6–10 units) may occur in advanced Paget's disease, osteopetrosis, hyperparathyroidism, and carcinoma of the breast with metastases to the bone. Mildly increased values in these cases are probably due to the measurable activity of high concentrations of alkaline phosphatase at pH 4.9.

Normal Values

1. Alkaline phosphatase: Adults, 4–10, K.A.U., children, 10–20 K.A.U.

2. Acid phosphatase: 0–4 K.A.U.

Notes and Precautions

The final blue color follows Beer's law at the selected wavelength, 660 mμ. A single standard solution is therefore sufficient for calibrating the photometer. For example, an absorbance reading of 0.308 was obtained when the alkaline phosphatase standard was measured in a Coleman No. 6–302 cuvette in the Coleman junior spectrophotometer. Accordingly, the calculation of alkaline phosphatase values may be simplified as follows:

$$\text{Units per 100 ml.} = \frac{25}{0.308} \times (R_A - R_B)$$

$$\text{Units per 100 ml.} = 81.2 \times (R_A - R_B)$$

The corresponding calculation for acid phosphatase is:

$$\text{Units per 100 ml.} = \frac{25}{0.616} \times (R_C - R_D)$$

$$\text{Units per 100 ml.} = 40.6 \times (R_C - R_D)$$

When other cuvettes or photometers are used, they should be individually calibrated in the same manner.

The range of alkaline phosphatase values which can be determined by this procedure includes 0–70 units. If higher levels are found (i.e., absorbance >1), an accurate value may be obtained by diluting 1 vol. of the final solution with 1 or 2 vol. of distilled water before measuring its absorbance. Multiplication by the dilution factor gives the factor to be used for these calculations.

Acid phosphatase values of 0–30 units can be determined by this procedure. Higher values may be determined also by dilution of the blue complex with distilled water before reading.

Although phenol has been used by others as a primary standard (direct weighing without standardization), this procedure is not recommended. Even "pure" desiccated phenol was found to contain less than 90% of the substance by weight.

Hemolyzed specimens of serum (plasma) should not be used for acid phosphatase determinations. Erythrocytes are known to contain large amounts of an acid phosphatase with optimal activity at pH 6 (5). Results may therefore be vitiated even by slight hemolysis.

Only very pure disodium phenyl phosphate, phenol-free, is suitable for use as substrate. The products marketed by the British Drug Houses, Ltd., London, England, and by Paul-Lewis Laboratories, Inc., New York have been found to be suitable. Very high blank readings were obtained with several other products.

Other methods of determination: Methods for the determination of alkaline phosphatase differ with regard to choice of (a) substrate, (b) buffer, (c) pH of the reaction, (d) time of incubation, and (e) the hydrolytic product to be measured.

Other substrates include glycerophosphate (6), phenolphthalein phosphate (7), p-nitrophenyl phosphate (8), and hexose phosphate (9). Of these, glycerophosphate has been the most widely used. In place of King's carbonate-bicarbonate buffer, veronal buffer (6) is frequently employed.

Bodansky (6) originally employed a pH of 8.6, but it was later demonstrated that optimum activity of alkaline phosphatase occurs in the vicinity of pH 9.3 (10). According to King (2) the optimum activity of this enzyme toward phenyl phosphate in carbonate-bicarbonate buffer is located at pH 10.0. It has been shown that the rate of enzymic hydrolysis and the optimum pH depend upon the nature of the substrate (11) and also upon the nature of the buffer (12).

Serum acid phosphatase activity is invariably measured at pH

4.9–5.0. Acetate buffer (10) may be substituted for citrate buffer, although the latter is preferred, since crystalline citric acid furnishes more nearly reproducible acid concentrations than does glacial acetic acid. The extent of hydrolysis is frequently measured by determining the amount of liberated phosphate. In this case, the acidity must be confined to a relatively narrow range during color development, in order to achieve reproducible values. Because oxalate interferes with the development of color, oxalated plasma should not be analyzed for phosphatase activity by this procedure. The method offers the advantage of providing a value for serum inorganic phosphate without additional effort.

BIBLIOGRAPHY

1. Folin, O., and Ciocalteu, V., *J. Biol. Chem.* **73:** 627 (1927).
2. King, E. J., *Micro-Analysis in Medical Biochemistry*, pp. 58–59, J. and A. Churchill, Ltd., London, 1946.
3. Gutman, E. B., and Gutman, A. B., *J. Biol. Chem.* **136:** 201 (1940).
4. Cantarow, A., and Trumper, M., *Clinical Biochemistry*, 4th ed., p. 198, W. B. Saunders Co., Philadelphia, 1950.
5. Sunderman, F. W., *Am. J. Clin. Pathol.* **12:** 404 (1942).
6. Bodansky, A., *J. Biol. Chem.* **99:** 197 (1932); **101:** 93 (1933).
7. Appelyard, J., *Biochem. J.* **42:** 596 (1948).
8. Bessey, O. A., Lowry, O. H., and Brock, M. J., *J. Biol. Chem.* **164:** 321 (1946).
9. Brachet, J., *Enzymologia* **11:** 336 (1945).
10. Shinowara, G. Y., Jones, L. M., and Reinhart, H. L., *J. Biol. Chem.* **142:** 921 (1942).
11. King, E. J., and Delory, G. E., *Biochem. J.* **33:** 1185 (1939).
12. Folley, S. J., and Kay, H. D., *Biochem. J.* **29:** 1837 (1935).

Inorganic Phosphate

Submitted by: MARSCHELLE H. POWER, Section of Biochemistry, Mayo Clinic, Rochester, Minnesota.

Checked by: NELSON F. YOUNG, Department of Clinical Pathology and Hospital Laboratories, Medical College of Virginia, Richmond, Virginia.

Author: G. GOMORI, *J. Lab. Clin. Med.* **27**: 955 (1941–1942).

Introduction

The method depends on the reduction of the easily reducible phosphomolybdic acid complex to produce blue color proportional to the amount of phosphate present. After extensive experience with other procedures based on this principle, the use of Elon was considered as the reducing agent representing the most satisfactory version of these methods. Gomori states that the results in many hundreds of analyses of serum or tissues were in excellent agreement with those obtained by the methods of Fiske and SubbaRow (1) and of Kuttner and Cohen (2). In comparison with these methods, however, the use of Elon possesses several advantages, such as easy availability and relative stability of the reducing agent, lower sensitivity to non-phosphate substances, and reliability throughout a greater range of acidity.

Reagents

1. *Trichloroacetic acid:* 5% in distilled water.

2. *Molybdate-sulfuric acid:* Dissolve 5 g. of sodium molybdate ($Na_2MoO_4 \cdot 2H_2O$) in about 500 ml. of distilled water, add 50 ml. of 10 N sulfuric acid, and make the volume to 1000 ml. with water.

3. *Reducing agent:* Dissolve 1 g. of Elon (*p*-methylaminophenol sulfate, Eastman Kodak, Practical, No. P615) in 100 ml. of 3% solution of sodium bisulfite. Gomori states that this solution is stable more or less indefinitely. It has been our practice, however, to prepare it fresh about every four weeks. The solution should be filtered through Whatman No. 40 or No. 42 filter paper.

4. Standard phosphate, stock solution: This solution contains 0.4394 g. of potassium dihydrogen phosphate (KH_2PO_4) in 1000 ml. of solution, equivalent to 0.100 mg. of phosphorus per milliliter.

Procedure

1. Preparation of protein-free filtrate: To 1.00 ml. of serum in a clean dry test tube add 9.00 ml. of trichloroacetic acid (reagent 1), mix the contents of the tube thoroughly, and after about 5–10 minutes, filter through a small Whatman No. 40 filter paper. It is good practice in general to discard the first milliliter or so of filtrate.

2. Development of color: If the Coleman junior spectrophotometer is available, it is convenient to develop color directly in 19 × 105 mm. cuvettes. Mix 2.00 ml. of the protein-free filtrate and 5.00 ml. of molybdate-sulfuric acid solution (reagent 2) in a cuvette. Add 0.25 ml. of Elon (reagent 3), and mix thoroughly. At the same time, prepare a reference blank consisting of 2.00 ml. of trichloroacetic acid (reagent 1), 5.00 ml. of reagent 2, and 0.25 ml. of reagent 3, similarly mixed in a cuvette. Allow the mixtures to stand 45 minutes or longer for development of full color, after which the per cent transmittance of the unknown at 700 mμ may be determined, first adjusting the galvanometer to read 100 with the blank in the light path.

Calculation

It is convenient to convert transmittance values to inorganic phosphate phosphorus by means of a calibration curve or a tabulation of transmittance versus phosphorus. To prepare such a curve, transfer 2.00-, 4.00-, 6.00-, 8.00-, 10.00-, 12.00-, and 15.00-ml. portions of stock standard (reagent 4) to 100-ml. volumetric flasks, and make the volume in each flask up to the mark with distilled water. After mixing the contents of each flask thoroughly, transfer a 2.00-ml. portion of each to a 19 × 105 mm. cuvette. Place 2 ml. of distilled water in another cuvette for the blank. Color is developed in the standards and the blank by addition of 5.00 ml. of reagent 2 and 0.25 ml. of reagent 3 to each cuvette, exactly as described above. Read transmittance values at 700 mμ after about 45 minutes, with reference to the reagent blank set at 100. The amount of phosphate phosphorus in the cuvettes corresponds to 0.004, 0.008, 0.012, 0.016, 0.020, 0.024, and 0.030 mg., respectively; or to 2, 4, 6, 8, 10, 12, and 15 mg. of phosphorus per 100 ml. of serum, when 2 ml. of filtrate prepared as directed are used. Representative readings, under the conditions described, were as follows: 79.5, 64.0, 50.5, 41.3, 32.8, 26.9, and 18.8% transmittance, respectively. These values, when plotted vertically on semi-log paper against concentrations horizontally, conform well to a straight line passing through 100 on the transmittance scale.

Comments

Gomori defines "acid tolerance" in terms of the permissible range of milliliters of normal sulfuric acid (milliequivalents) per 10 mg. of sodium molybdate. This range extends from 0.9 to 2.2 for Elon, in comparison with 1.1 to 2.1 for the method of Fiske and SubbaRow, and only 1.3 to 1.45 for the method of Kuttner and Cohen. As long as the ratio between acid and molybdate is maintained within the limits indicated, actual concentrations of acid and molybdate may vary considerably without affecting the amount of color produced by a given amount of phosphate. For example, if the final concentration of molybdate is 0.25%, concentration of acid may range from 0.25 to 0.50 N; or if molybdate is 0.50% acid may range from slightly below 0.50 N to slightly above 1.0 N; etc. The flexibility of the procedure in these respects obviates the use of several different molybdate solutions for use with samples of different acidity, such as was incorporated in the method of Fiske and SubbaRow. We have fully confirmed Gomori's claims as to "acid tolerance" but have noted that development of color may be somewhat slower at the high acidity of 1.0 N, particularly if the acid molybdate ratio is as high as 2.0.

Full color is developed in 45 minutes and is stable thereafter for an hour or longer. If necessary, useful data can be obtained in a shorter time.

The procedure as described has been used for several years and for several thousands of determinations of inorganic phosphate in serum in the routine laboratories. It has also been eminently satisfactory in the Bodansky procedure for phosphatase and, because of high acid tolerance, in the determination of lipid phosphorus (3).

Range of values

In 100 presumably healthy blood donors studied at the Medical College of Virginia, the range of values for inorganic phosphate in serum was found to be 2.4–4.7 mg. of phosphorus per 100 ml. of serum, and the mean, 3.68 mg.%; 89 of the values fell between 3.2 and 4.3 mg.%, 3 being above and 8 below this range. Duplicate filtrates were prepared, and only one set of duplicates failed to check within 5%. Recovery of phosphate added to either normal or uremic sera was satisfactory.

As illustrative of the values encountered in a clinic population, 100 consecutive analyses based on preparation of a single filtrate were selected for study. Determinations on the sera of children or of patients with hypo- or hyperparathyroidism or with serum calcium values below 9.0 mg. % were excluded from consideration. The range observed extended from 2.25 to 5.00 mg. % phosphorus. The mean value was 3.47, with standard deviation of ±0.606, indicating, as might be expected, a somewhat greater variability than was seen in the group of presumably healthy subjects.

BIBLIOGRAPHY

1. Fiske, C. H., and SubbaRow, Y., J. Biol. Chem. **66:** 375 (1925).
2. Kuttner, T. T., and Cohen, H. R., J. Biol. Chem. **75:** 517 (1927).
3. Maclay, Elizabeth, Am. J. Med. Technol. **17:** 265 (1951).

Total Protein, Albumin, and Globulin

Submitted by: JOHN G. REINHOLD, Pepper Laboratory of Clinical Medicine, Hospital of the University of Pennsylvania, Philadelphia, Pennsylvania.

Checked by: CAPT. DAVID SELIGSON, CAPT. GEORGE E. SCHREINER, LOIS V. RIDDLE, and WILLIAM SHARON, Army Medical Service Graduate School, Walter Reed Army Medical Center, Washington, D. C. MARGARET VANDERAU, Presbyterian Hospital, Philadelphia, Pennsylvania.

Authors: G. R. KINGSLEY, *J. Biol. Chem.* **131:** 197 (1939).
J. G. REINHOLD, V. S. STEWARD, and L. GILMAN, Abstracts of the Philadelphia Meeting, American Chemical Society, April 9–13, 1950.
T. E. WEICHSELBAUM, *Am. J. Clin. Pathol.* **7:** 40 (1946).

Introduction

This method is adapted from that of Kingsley, who was among the first to describe a practical method for applying the biuret reaction to the quantitative measurement of serum protein concentrations. In 1940 Kingsley (1) also introduced the use of ether for effecting rapid separation of albumin and globulin by means of salt solutions and demonstrated that salting-out could be done at room temperature. The biuret reagent of Kingsley was modified by Weichselbaum (1946), to improve its stability and to decrease formation of turbidity by serum. For these reasons, it is used in the method described here.

Soon after the introduction of the electrophoretic method for separation of proteins of serum, it became clear that the 21.5% sodium sulfate solution proposed by Howe (2) or the half-saturated ammonium solution used by most European laboratories for salting-out globulins failed to make a complete separation. Majoor (3) and Milne (4) improved the accuracy of the salting out procedure by the use of higher concentrations of sodium sulfate. However, the solutions used by them crystallized readily at room temperature and this necessitated that they be used at 37°C. This disadvantage has been overcome in this method by the use of a mixture of sodium sulfate and sulfite, the solubilities being additive. The mixed salt solution can be used in combination with ether for rapid separation of globulin and albumin. It has the additional advantage of being well buffered by the sodium sulfite, whereas sodium sulfate solutions are subject to large changes in pH if contaminated with small amounts of acid or alkali. This has been an occasional cause of large errors in applying older methods.

Reagents

1. Stock biuret reagent, Weichselbaum: Dissolve 45 g. of sodium potassium tartrate (Rochelle salt) in approximately 400 ml. of 0.2 N NaOH. Add 15 g. of $CuSO_4 \cdot 5H_2O$ as fine crystals while stirring, and continue stirring until the copper is completely dissolved. Add 5 g. of KI, and dilute to 1000 ml. with 0.2 N NaOH.

2. Dilute biuret solution: Dilute 200 ml. of the stock biuret solution to 1000 ml. with 0.2 N sodium hydroxide containing 5 g. KI per liter.

3. Sodium hydroxide, (1) 0.2 N and (2) 0.2 N with 0.5% KI: Prepare from carbonate-free concentrated sodium hydroxide solution. Titrate against 0.1 N acid. Add 5 g. of KI per liter to obtain (2).

4. Tartrate-iodide solution for serum blank: Dissolve 9 g. of Rochelle salt in 0.2 N sodium hydroxide with 0.5% KI, and dilute to 1000 ml.

5. Standard serum: Pool normal or pathological sera, and standardize by Kjeldahl or gravimetric methods. Measure 2-ml. portions into test tubes. Stopper tightly, and store in deep freeze or freezer (ice-cube) compartment of refrigerator.

6. Ether: Reagent quality is preferred but not indispensable. The alcohol content must not be excessive.

Total Protein

Procedure

Measure 5.0 ml. of biuret reagent (or minimal quantity required for photometer reading), using a volumetric or automatic pipette, into a standard cuvette. Add 0.1 ml. of serum measured exactly from a calibrated Folin micro or other high precision pipette calibrated to contain. Rinse the pipette with the biuret reagent several times. Place the cuvettes in a water bath at 30–32° C. for 10 minutes. Measure absorbance (color density), using a 555-mμ filter (a 540-mμ filter may be substituted). Use the biuret blank for the zero setting.

1. Serum blank: Measure 5 ml. (or same volume as biuret reagent) of the tartrate-iodide blank solution into a cuvette. Add 0.1 ml. of serum. The serum blank is essential only when pigmented or opalescent specimens are examined, but accuracy is improved by including it routinely. Use tartrate-iodide solution for the zero setting.

2. Biuret blank: Measure 5 ml. of biuret reagent (or same volume as biuret reagent). Add 0.1 ml. of distilled water. Proceed as described for serum.

3. Serum standard: Treat a serum of known protein concentration according to the directions given for the unknown serums. Include a serum blank.

Calculation

$$\text{Protein, g. per 100 ml.} = (U - B_u)\,\frac{C}{(S - B_s)}$$

where U is the absorbance of the unknown, S of the standard serum, B_s of the standard's blank, and B_u of the serum blank. C is the concentration of protein in the standard serum in grams per 100 ml.

TOTAL PROTEIN, ALBUMIN, AND GLOBULIN

Reagents

1. Dilute biuret solution, tartrate-iodide solution.

2. Sulfate-sulfite solution: Place 208 g. of sodium sulfate and 70 g. of sodium sulfite in a flask or beaker of 2-l. capacity. Add to 900 ml. of water in a separate container 2 ml. of concentrated sulfuric acid. Add the acidified water without delay to the salts while stirring. When dissolved, transfer to a volumetric flask, and dilute to 1000 ml. with water. The pH is not critical provided that it is above 7. (Before measuring pH, dilute 1 ml. to 25 ml. with water.) Store in glass-stoppered bottles at temperatures exceeding 25° C.

3. Standard serum: as described under total protein.

Procedure

All solutions and glassware must be kept at temperatures above 25° C. throughout. If room temperature is below this, crystallization of sodium sulfate may occur. (See note below.)

Measure 7.5 ml. of sulfate-sulfite solution into a test tube 18 × 120 mm. Add slowly, and with continuous mixing, 0.5 ml. of serum. Stopper, and mix by inverting. Immediately remove 2 ml. of the mixture for total protein determination, and add it to 5 ml. of biuret reagent in a cuvette. Pour 3 ml. of ether into the tube containing the remaining serum sulfate-sulfite mixture. Stopper, and shake exactly 40 times in 20 seconds. Centrifuge 5–10 minutes at 2000 rpm.

Tilt the tube to permit insertion of a pipette into the clear solution below the layer of globulin and, without disturbing the precipitate, remove 2 ml. of the solution and add it to a cuvette containing 5 ml. of biuret reagent (or other convenient volume).

1. Serum blank: Add 2 ml. of serum suspension to 5 ml. of tartrate iodide. Mix. Usually this step can be omitted, but if the specimen is opalescent or excessively pigmented, it must be included. Accuracy is improved by including it routinely.

2. Standard: Treat 0.5 ml. of standardized serum as described above, and remove 2 ml. as described for total protein determination. Omit the remainder of the fractionation procedure.

3. Biuret blank: Add 2 ml. of sulfate-sulfite solution to 5 ml. of biuret reagent.

4. Color development: Place the tubes containing biuret and blank solutions in a water bath at 30–32° C. for 10 minutes. Cool at room temperature 5 minutes. Read the color density at 555 mμ (540 or 565 mμ may be employed). Read the serum blanks first. Then, with the biuret blank in position, adjust the photocolorimeter to a zero setting before reading the unknowns.

Calculation

$$\text{Protein, g. per 100 ml.} = (U - B_u) \frac{C}{(S - B_s)}$$

where U is the absorbance of the unknown, S of the standard, B_u

and B_s the densities of the blank tubes for unknown and standard, respectively.

Albumin = Protein remaining in sulfate-sulfite solution.
Globulin = Total protein − albumin.

Comments

No difficulty will be encountered due to the crystallization of sodium sulfate from the sulfate-sulfite solution provided that (a) solutions are prepared from anhydrous sodium sulfate and the solutions do not come in contact with $Na_2SO_4 \cdot 10H_2O$ and (b) temperatures of the solutions are kept above 25°C. at all stages. It may be convenient during cold months to work in a hood in which there is a steam-heated water bath. Cracking the steam valve keeps the temperatures safely above the minimum. It is helpful to store the sulfate-sulfite solution at 37° C. until used. Warm water can be placed in the centrifuge cups if the centrifuge is in a cool location. The salting out should be carried through without interruption, for delay favors crystallization and it is desirable to analyze no more samples than can be handled expeditiously in a single run. From our experience this will be 12–16 tubes.

The most critical operation in the method is the shaking of the serum-salt mixture with ether. This must be done exactly as specified. Violent shaking should be avoided, for experience has shown that it will cause denaturation of albumin. An excursion of the arm of about 15 inches, 40 times, 2 times to the second, is optimal. An error of 2 or 3 seconds in timing will not affect the results, but shaking for less than 15 seconds or for more than 25 will cause the method to give albumin values that are high or low, respectively.

The tubes should be stoppered or firmly capped during the centrifugation to prevent accumulation of ether fumes in the vicinity of the centrifuge. The centrifuge should be run at a speed sufficient to give a firm layer of globulin that will not disintegrate when the tube is tilted and the albumin solution removed.

Pipetting the albumin solution from below the globulin precipitate must be done without touching the globulin layer. The precipitated globulin readily adheres to the pipette and must be carefully wiped off if such contact is made.

Color development is nearly complete after warming for 10 minutes at 30° C., and the results are the same as those obtained when the color is allowed to develop 30 minutes, as suggested by Weichselbaum. Besides the saving in time so effected, turbidity increases in some specimens during the period of heating, and therefore the shorter time is preferred.

The color formed by the biuret reagent per gram of albumin is so nearly identical with that formed by globulin that the same standard can be used for both. A slightly greater color density produced by albumin is counterbalanced by an increase in the volume of the solution caused by saturating it with ether.

Pooled surplus serum remaining after analyses are completed has been used by us for many years as a source of standard. The serum should be refrigerated until the pool is complete, then centrifuged after being held in the refrigerator an additional 24 hours. The clear supernatant is decanted from any sediment. The protein concentration is determined by the method of Hiller, Plazin, and Van Slyke (5). Protein nitrogen is multiplied by 6.25 to obtain a value for serum protein. The pool is then divided into 2-ml. portions and stored in a deep freeze in tubes at $-15°$ C. or other convenient temperature below freezing. The serum is thawed at 42–46° C. just before use. Any unused surplus is discarded, for deterioration may be rapid in the thawed samples. Thorough mixing by pouring from one tube to another is a most important preliminary to removal of aliquots for analysis.

Significance: Serum total protein is used for detection of hypoproteinemia as a cause of or contributing factor in edema and for evaluating the extent of protein depletion due to massive albuminuria, bleeding, transudation, neoplastic and other wasting diseases, and malnutrition. It is useful also for detecting hyperproteinemia caused by dehydration and hemoconcentration, and for detecting hyperglobulinemia due to multiple myeloma, sarcoidosis, lymphogranuloma, liver diseases, parasitic infections, and the numerous other diseases accompanied by high globulin concentrations.

Total protein determinations may be used for following changes in hydration in post-operative patients and patients suffering from burns or other injuries, and, together with other factors, for partial evaluation of types and amounts of fluids required for administration to the patient. In this connection and also in the detection of plasma protein depletion, it is subject to inaccuracies caused by changes in plasma volume.

Separate determination of albumin and globulin is indicated in nearly all circumstances where abnormalities of more than short duration in plasma protein metabolism are suspected. Frequently, as in cirrhosis of the liver, albumin will decrease in concentration to the same extent that globulin increases, so that total protein concentrations remain within the limits found in healthy individuals. Thus, separate measurements of serum albumin and globulin increase the sensitivity with which change in protein composition may be detected and the accuracy with which the results can be interpreted. Once the albumin and globulin concentrations have been established, total protein determinations will often suffice for studies made at short time intervals.

Other methods: Numerous methods have been described for determination of serum protein. The method universally recognized as standard is the Kjeldahl nitrogen determination. A reliable technique for using it was described by Hiller, Plazin, and Van Slyke (5). Methods based on specific gravity are widely used, especially since the introduction of the copper sulfate method by Phillips and associates (6), but specific gravity of serum may be affected by other components. Gravimetric methods have been used to some extent, but they are too time-consuming for clinical use. Refractometry is also unsuitable for clinical work because of large errors caused mainly by lipids.

Methods based on tyrosine, arginine, or any specific amino acid component of protein are subject to error because of differences in chromogenic value of the various serum proteins. As the serum protein complex undergoes changes associated with disease, marked differences in reactivity will occur. The Folin phenol reagent used after preliminary treatment with alkaline copper reagent is extremely sensitive but suffers from this disadvantage [Lowry, Rosebrough, Farr, and Randall, (7)].

Ninhydrin has been used successfully as a highly sensitive reagent for serum total protein determination [Kunkel and Ward (8)].

The biuret reaction has numerous advantages over other procedures for measurement of serum protein, and Robinson and Hogden (9) have described an excellent method for applying the biuret method to this purpose. It is more time-consuming than the present method because protein is first separated by precipitation before being treated with the biuret reagent. Gornall, Bardawill, and David (10) have described a modified biuret reagent.

For separate determination of albumin and globulin, the Tiselius electrophoretic method is the accepted standard. The method here described has been standardized by comparing the results with those obtained by the electrophoretic method in over 100 widely varied pathological sera. The average albumin obtained by the salting-out method using sulfate-sulfite is nearly identical with that of the electrophoretic method. Differences seldom exceed 0.5 g., a value anticipated on the basis of the precision of the electrophoretic method. The salting-out method deviates from the electrophoretic beyond this limit only when the gamma globulin is abnormally low, which causes the albumin to be high, or when the gamma globulin is extremely high (8 gm. per 100 ml. or higher), when albumin measured by this method is too low.

Sodium sulfate in high concentrations was used by Majoor and Milne at 37° C. temperatures, but filtration was used for separating globulin. Wolfson, Cohn, and coworkers (11) have used sodium sulfite in 28% solution together with ether for rapid separation of albumin from globulin. Preparation of 28% solutions of sodium sulfite is time-consuming and therefore less convenient than the use of sulfate-sulfite mixtures. Sodium sulfite as a reagent for separating proteins was introduced by Campbell and Hanna (12).

We have found that ammonium sulfate, sodium or potassium phosphate, or magnesium sulfate solutions used as reagents for salting-out globulins interfere with application of the biuret reaction.

Several methods based on the use of alcohol for separation of protein fractions according to principles developed in Cohn's laboratory have been described by Cohn and associates (13). Precise control of temperatures in the −5° C. range is essential at all stages of the separation. Unless suitable refrigerated equipment is at hand, results obtained by such methods are unreliable. This applies also to the method of Pillemer and Hutchinson (14), which substitutes methanol for ethanol. Recently the use of hematin as a specific reagent for albumin has been described by Rosenfeld and Surgenor (15).

RESULTS OBTAINED USING THE SODIUM SULFATE-SULFITE METHOD

This method for serum proteins (total, albumin, and globulin) has proved to be simple to execute, accurate, and rapid. Standards are prepared from pooled serum on which the total and non-protein nitrogen is measured, respectively, by macro and micro Kjeldahl procedures. With each analysis the standard is included in the days' work and is used as the reference. Data on forty-two normal

TABLE I

TOTAL SERUM PROTEIN, ALBUMIN, AND GLOBULIN MEASUREMENTS ON FORTY-TWO NORMAL PERSONS

	Total protein, g/100 ml.	Albumin, g/100 ml.	Globulin, g/100 ml.	Ratio
Mean	7.14	4.19	2.9	1.43
Actual range	6.5–7.7	3.9–4.6	2.3–3.5	1.18–1.87
*Theoretical range	6.6–7.6	3.8–4.6	2.4–3.5	1.13–1.73
S. D.	0.24	0.19	0.26	0.15

* Mean ± 2 S.D.

TABLE II

Type of patient	No.	Total protein g/100 ml.		Albumin g/100 ml.		Globulin g/100 ml.		A/G ratio	
		Range	Mean	Range	Mean	Range	Mean	Range	Mean
*Control	19	6.23–7.03	6.66	2.98–4.45	3.98	2.18–3.66	2.67	0.81–1.8	1.52
Arterio-venous fistulas	34	6.02–7.14	6.62	3.37–4.49	3.84	2.29–3.51	2.78	1.16–1.78	1.39
Postoperative A-V fistulas	26	5.87–7.09	6.56	3.56–4.37	3.77	2.14–3.39	2.79	1.01–1.85	1.37
	79		6.61		3.84		2.75		1.43

* Hospitalized patients corresponding to the above patients but having no A-V fistulas.

persons are shown in Table I. Electrophoresis analyses reveal on normal and abnormal serums moderately good agreement.

Tests on replicability reveal that daily changes of total protein albumin and globulin are perhaps due to water changes in that the albumin/globulin ratio remains remarkably constant even though there may be a daily change in total protein of 10%.

The reliability of any single value (total protein, albumin, or globulin) is better than 5% of the absolute.

From a clinical point of view this method has provided excellent data for following the course of liver disease. In convalescent and acute hepatitis the albumin, globulin, and A/G ratio remained abnormal longer than any other routine liver function test (50–120 days).

This method for measurement of plasma protein has been used in another laboratory in connection with physiologic studies for ambulatory and hospitalized patients. Standards have been measured in duplicate against another laboratory, and agreement within 0.1 g. has been obtained.

Data obtained in patients are summarized in Table II.

In addition, the method was used to measure the change in serum protein following saline. In the procedure the decrease in total protein (Δ g.) averaged 0.52 and the decrease in albumin (Δ g.) averaged 0.35. Since mobilized extracellular fluid contains relatively more albumin, it is felt that the ratio of 0.67 adequately reflected the physiologic change in this experiment.

BIBLIOGRAPHY

•1. Kingsley, G. R., *J. Biol. Chem.* **133:** 731 (1940); *J. Lab. Clin. Med.* **27:** 840 (1942).
2. Howe, P. C., *J. Biol. Chem.* **49:** 109 (1921).
3. Majoor, C. E. H., *J. Biol. Chem.* **169:** 583 (1947).
4. Milne, J., *J. Biol. Chem.* **169:** 595 (1947).
5. Hiller, A., Plazin, J., and Van Slyke, D. D., *J. Biol. Chem.* **176:** 1401 (1948).
6. Phillips, R. A., Van Slyke, D. D., Hamilton, P. B., Dole, V. P., Emerson, K., Archibald, R. M., and Stanley, E. G., *J. Biol. Chem.* **183:** 305 (1950).
7. Lowry, O. H., Rosebrough, N. J., Farr, A. L., and Randall, R. J., *J. Biol. Chem.* **193:** 265 (1951).
8. Kunkel, H. G., and Ward, S. M., *J. Biol. Chem.* **182:** 597 (1950).
9. Robinson, H. W., and Hogden, C. G., *J. Biol. Chem.* **135:** 707, 727 (1940).
10. Gornall, A. G., Bardawill, C. J., and David, M. M., *J. Biol. Chem.* **177:** 751 (1949).
11. Wolfson, W. Q., Cohn, C., Calvery, E., and Zehiba, F., *Am. J. Clin. Pathol.* **18:** 723 (1948).
12. Campbell, W. R., and Hanna, M. I., *J. Biol. Chem.* **119:** 9 (1937).
13. Cohn, E. J., Gurd, F. R. N., Surgenor, D. M., Barnes, B. A., Brown, R. K., Derouaux, G., Gillespie, J. M., Kahnt, F. W., Lever, W. F., Liu, C. H., Mittelman, D., Mouton, R. F., Schmidt, K., and Uroma, E., *J. Am. Chem. Soc.* **72:** 465 (1950).
14. Pillemer, L., and Hutchinson, M. C., *J. Biol. Chem.* **158:** 299 (1945).
15. Rosenfeld, M. and Surgenor, D. M., *J. Biol. Chem.* **199:** 911 (1952).

Prothrombin Time*

Submitted by: LT. COMDR. H. C. SUDDUTH, Department of Physiological Chemistry, U.S. Naval Medical School, National Naval Medical Center, Bethesda, Maryland.

Checked by: MIRIAM REINER, Gallinger Municipal Hospital, Washington, D.C.

Author: S. SHAPIRO, *Exptl. Med. and Surg.* **2:** 103 (1944).

Introduction

Prothrombin is converted to thrombin in the presence of thromboplastin, calcium, and accessory clotting factors. The thrombin then catalyzes the transformation of fibrinogen into fibrin. The time necessary for the appearance of a fibrin clot after the addition of plasma to the thromboplastin and calcium mixture is an index of the prothrombin activity of the plasma. This is the Link-Shapiro modification of the Quick one-stage technique.

Reagents

1. Sodium oxalate, 0.1 M: Dissolve 13.40 g. of anhydrous sodium oxalate ($Na_2C_2O_4$), A.C.S., in 700 or 800 ml. of distilled water, in a 1-l. volumetric flask. Dilute to volume.

2. Thromboplastin: Any good thromboplastin preparation, giving consistent values (within 1 second) on normal plasma. Preparations are available containing the proper amount of calcium.

3. Normal saline, 0.9% NaCl c.p.

4. Calcium chloride, 0.02 M: 0.002 g. $CaCl_2$, c.p. anhydrous in 100 ml. of water if thromboplastin preparation does not contain calcium.

5. Prothrombin-free plasma: To each milliliter of fresh normal plasma add 0.1 g. of barium sulfate powder. Shake the mixture thoroughly, and place in an incubator at 37° C. for 15 minutes. Shake at frequent intervals while it is in the incubator. Remove, and centrifuge for 30 minutes at 3000 rpm, after which the supernatant is carefully separated. This prothrombin-free plasma, used

---

* The opinions and conclusions contained in this report are those of the authors, and not necessarily those of the Department of the Navy.

as a diluent, should be kept at refrigerator temperature (4°–5° C.) and should be used within 5 hours after preparation.

Procedure

1. Preparation of blood sample:

(a) Place 0.5 ml. of 0.1 *M* sodium oxalate solution into a special test tube calibrated at 5 ml.

(b) Add 4.5 ml. of blood rapidly to the sodium oxalate solution.

(c) Centrifuge at 1700 rpm for 10 minutes.

(d) Pipette off the clear plasma into a test tube, and determine the prothrombin activity as soon as practicable. If longer than 30 minutes will elapse before the determination can be done, do not pipette off the plasma, but place the entire tube after centrifugation into the refrigerator.

(e) If the prothrombin activity of the dilute (12.5%) plasma is desired, mix 1 ml. of the patient's whole plasma·with 7 ml. of a prepared diluent, such as prothrombin-free plasma or saline. Similarly, other dilutions may be prepared.

2. Prothrombin time determination:

(a) Using a serological pipette, place 0.2 ml. of the thromboplastin suspension containing calcium chloride into each of two 12 × 75 mm. test tubes. This is sufficient for duplicate determinations of prothrombin activity of plasma from one patient.

(b) Place the two test tubes in a water bath maintained at 37° C. About 3 minutes is sufficient to bring the tube contents to the temperature of the water bath.

(c) A test tube containing the whole or diluted blood plasma to be tested is placed in a water bath at 37° C. for 3 minutes.

(d) With a micropipette (blood sugar), take 0.1 ml. of whole blood plasma (or dilution). Hold the pipette just above the liquid in one of the two tubes containing the thromboplastin. Blow out the pipette quickly to deliver the contents, and at the same instant start the stopwatch (preferably operated by a foot pedal). Tap the tube sharply to mix the contents while it is in the water bath. Keep it in the bath throughout the rest of the procedure. Move a small wire-loop stirrer in slow sweeps across the bottom of the test tube, and observe it against a strong light set at an optimum angle behind the water bath. When the clot adheres to the wire loop, stop the watch, and record the time. Repeat the test with the remaining tube of thromboplastin suspension.

(e) Perform duplicate determinations on normal plasma. Reconstituted lyophilized plasma preparations may be used.

When thromboplastin which does not contain calcium chloride is used, then the addition of reagents is as follows: 0.1 ml. of thromboplastin is put into the tubes, then 0.1 ml. of patient's plasma is added. Incubate at 37° C., and add 0.1 ml. of 0.02 M calcium chloride. Start the stopwatch and proceed as above.

Calculation

The prothrombin time of the patient, and of the normal plasma, is reported. Because of the hyperbolic nature of the prothrombin concentration-time curve, and the variation in curves obtained from different subjects, "per cent of normal activity" is not a very meaningful figure.

Comments

The whole plasma prothrombin time is useful in following patients on dicumarol therapy. The therapeutic range for prothrombin time is 30–40 seconds, when a thromboplastin giving a normal range of 13–15 seconds is used. Prothrombin times over 50 seconds are dangerous and should be called to the attention of the attending physician immediately. Dilute (12.5%) prothrombin times are normally between 35 and 45 seconds.

The prothrombin time is also helpful in the diagnosis of vitamin K deficiency and liver damage. In both these conditions the prothrombin time is prolonged. In the initial stages, prolongation may be more evident in the dilute prothrombin time.

The vitamin K tolerance test for liver damage depends on the laboratory determination of prothrombin time, while the prothrombin consumption test for hemophilia and thrombocytopenic purpura is based on a comparison of plasma and serum prothrombin times.

Factors Affecting Prothrombin Time

1. Temperature: This must be kept near 37° C. throughout the period of stirring. The thromboplastin solution is inactivated if kept at 37° C. for more than about 30 minutes, so it should be incubated just before use, and the main batch kept under constant refrigeration. As mentioned under Procedure, the prothombin time is likely to be prolonged if the blood remains at room temperature more than a few minutes.

2. Stirring: The number of sweeps per second of the wire loop must be carefully controlled at a uniform rate.

3. Plasma factors other than prothrombin: A prolonged prothrombin time may be caused by a deficiency of fibrinogen, Ac-globulin, or other accessory blood clotting factors. In these cases the whole plasma prothrombin time may be prolonged, the saline-diluted plasma prothrombin time prolonged, and the prothrombin-free plasma-diluted prothrombin time is essentially normal. Calcium deficiency has never been known to produce an abnormal prothrombin time.

4. Glassware: This must be clean. Special care must be used in rinsing glassware free of all detergents.

5. Collection of the sample: A clean venipuncture should be performed, as tissue juices accelerate the clotting time, and may cause false values to be obtained.

Sodium and Potassium by Flame Photometry

Submitted by: JOSEPH BENOTTI, Pratt Diagnostic Clinic, New England Medical Center, Boston, Massachusetts.

Introduction

The flame photometer, next to antibiotics, plays one of the chief roles of importance in the advance of modern medicine. As the name implies, it is an instrument that is similar in many ways to a photoelectric colorimeter. In the ordinary colorimeter the source of light is a bulb, whereas in the flame photometer the light source is the flame. The photometer measures light emitted from a flame at a definite wavelength.

The working principle of a simple flame photometer is as follows: The sample of liquid to be analyzed is atomized and passed directly into a non-luminous flame, each element giving off its own spectrum. By means of filters or some other monochromatic system, this light emitted from the burning elements can be directed upon one or more photocells. This in turn gives rise to electrical energy, which then deflects a galvanometer. The deflection is quantitated against the deflection produced by known solutions.

The atomizer is one of the most important parts of the instrument. Most atomizers work simply by passing a small stream of solution into a current of compressed air. Some atomizers are gravity-fed from a reservoir overhead; others draw the liquid up through a capillary by passing a stream of air or oxygen over the tip of the capillary, causing the necessary suction for the solution to rise from a reservoir below. In either case, the end result should be a very fine, dry spray. The wetting power of this atomized product seems to depend upon the droplet size. Hence, a very fine spray is necessary in order to avoid delivering larger droplets into the burner. The atomizer usually delivers varying sizes of droplets near the orifices of the air and liquid jets. However, by some system of baffles, the larger droplets may be prevented from traveling too far and thus reaching the flame.   It is of further advantage to have an atomizer which does not consume too much liquid.   There are many times, particularly in pediatrics, when there is not enough blood serum for macroanalysis.   Open-system atomizers should be avoided, since they allow contamination from the room to enter the base of the burner.   It is surprising how much sodium and potassium can be picked up from the atmosphere, probably from dust particles.   The best atomizers employ a closed system, thereby eliminating contamination.

The type of flame used is important for good results.   In general, the higher the temperature of the flame, the better is the spectrum emission.   For sodium and potassium analysis, however, an extremely hot flame is not essential, since these elements are easily excited.   Most of the instruments on the market require a very special type of flame, usually employing propane or acetylene and oxygen.   The reason for this is primarily that a hot flame is necessary to excite elements such as calcium and magnesium.   However, sodium and potassium give off good emission spectra even with city gas.   In order to get good constant emission, the flame must burn at a constant temperature.   This can be controlled best by having a pressure-regulating valve in the gas line with an appropriate gauge so that any fluctuations may be observed.   Since city gas is relatively impure (compared with propane and acetylene), it is of definite advantage to wash the gas.   This may be accomplished by bubbling it through water to remove dust particles or other solid impurities which may be present.   Such a procedure insures a flame of uniform blue, free of luminous flecks.   It is important to regulate the burner so that it burns with small pin-pointed cones at the grid, as this gives the hottest flame.

In order to enclose the burner completely and thus prevent contamination from the room reaching the flame, it should be surrounded by a glass chimney sealed at the bottom of the burner. This necessitates feeding the burner with air to keep it burning with a constant blue flame.

Since the instrument utilizes the fine atomized spray which is fed to the burner, the air supply used for atomizing must also be free from contamination.   Most large laboratories have a compressed air system piped directly to the laboratory.   Such a system is usually adequate, except for the fact that periodically it may deliver varying quantities of rust, water, or other impurities. Commercial filters are available which will remove these, but they in turn must be renewed from time to time. A very simple and inexpensive air filter may be constructed by passing the air through a 3-gallon carboy half-filled with water. To freshen such a filter, one simply replenishes it with distilled water.

Direct and Indirect Analysis

Flame photometers may be used by employing only one cell (in direct analysis), or they may be used with two (in indirect analysis), both of which are attached to the same galvanometer. In the direct method, only one cell is connected to the galvanometer so that the light which passes through the filter produces a definite deflection in the galvanometer in one direction. This deflection is compared to a known deflection for quantitation. In the indirect method, a known amount of foreign ion, such as lithium, is added to the solution to be analyzed. It burns with a very characteristic red color. By a proper system of filters, one can select the lithium light and allow it to strike a photocell. Simultaneously, the light from an unknown ion such as sodium or potassium may be focused on another photocell. Both photocells are connected to the same galvanometer, one tending to deflect the needle to the right, and the other to the left. By interposing a potentiometer into one of the circuits, one can readily control the galvanometer at the null point reading. One can quantitate the potentiometer readings against appropriate standards, all of which contain the same amount of lithium.

The indirect system of analysis is more accurate for simple flame photometers. There are several reasons for this: (1) When a sample of serum or urine is atomized for any one element, there are many other ions present which may burn and give off their respective emission bands. These different sources of light interfere with each other, and thus some of the light is impeded from reaching the photocell. This may be described as an interference phenomenon. By introducing a definite amount of a foreign ion, such as lithium, in both the standard and the unknown, a comparable interference is assumed which cancels itself. (2) The instruments that use this system of analysis usually are wired electrically to the galvanometer in such a way that sodium or potassium tends to produce a deflection in one direction, whereas lithium deflects in the other direction. If the instrument is connected to the indirect system of analysis and a sample of solution is introduced into the atomizer, all the ions, including the lithium, make their way to the flame. Here each ion gives off its own spectrum emission. The sodium photocell picks up the sodium light and tends to send the galvanometer one way, while the lithium cell picks up the lithium light and tends to send the galvanometer the other way. Obviously, if the electrical energy created is equal, the galvanometer does not deflect. If one exceeds the other, the potentiometer may be adjusted so that the galvanometer assumes a null point reading. The advantage gained is that any minor fluctuations in the atomizer would certainly change the amount of sodium as well as the amount of lithium reaching the flame. Since both are changed equally, the galvanometer deflection should be practically negligible.

The following description pertains to the Barclay or a similar instrument, since that has been in use in the laboratory of the author.

Fundamentally, the instrument is well designed, having three photocells—one for sodium, one for potassium, and one for lithium—connected with a very sensitive galvanometer. The switches connecting the various photocells to the galvanometer, either for direct or indirect measurement, may give trouble from time to time, as a result of poor contact. This phenomenon may be detected very easily either by the failure of the galvanometer to respond to a definite excitation of sodium or potassium, or by the gross nonreproducibility of calibration curves. When this happens, the front panel which holds the switches should be removed and the points filed with emery paper or some other abrasive.

The Barclay instrument comes with an atomizer which has definite limitations. First, it is not a closed atomizer and therefore allows contamination from the room to get into the flame, thus making the galvanometer fluctuate unnecessarily. Second, the atomizer is gravity-fed and must be rinsed between samples with the new solution in order to avoid contamination. Third, it uses quite a large amount of solution per minute, therefore making good sodium and potassium microdeterminations practically impossible.

The burner on the Barclay comes equipped for burning propane. This proves satisfactory, except when the hospital is unable to stock propane gas in the laboratory because it provides an extra fire hazard. Usually, gas is piped in from the outside. Furthermore, the tank may run out of gas occasionally and cause an interruption of service and great inconvenience.

These inherent weaknesses have been overcome by the construction of another atomizer. A good atomizer should have the following characteristics: It should (1) use small amounts of solution, (2) feed upward by suction so that no funnel rinsing is necessary, (3) use a small amount of air pressure (approximately 5 lb.) so that a large capacity air pressure pump is not necessary, (4) be completely closed to the atmosphere so that contamination in the room cannot get into the flame, (5) give a very fine, uniform spray which does not wet beyond the atomizing chamber, (6) be made of glass to prevent corrosion, (7) not easily clog, and (8) be so constructed so that it can be taken apart readily for occasional cleaning.

An all-glass atomizer (Fig. 1) which fulfills the above qualifications has been constructed. The air, at approximately 5 lb. pressure, enters the atomizer through tube A. By passing over capillary tube B at just the right angle, a suction is created in this tube, thereby allowing the solution to flow upward and thus become atomized. Some of the spray, particularly the larger droplets, condenses on the chamber walls and runs off as waste through tube C. The dry atomizer spray rises through tube D and flows over through tube E. This latter tube connects to the burner assembly by means of a short piece of rubber tubing. All the air that is necessary for complete combustion must come through the atomizer. Since the atomizer itself consumes a small amount of air, a small auxiliary inlet tube F is necessary to supply enough air for the burner. Obviously, in order to get proper and uniform burning, one must have rigid control of the amount of air entering tube F so that it may be kept constant. This is facilitated by means of a separate reducing valve and air pressure gauge as shown in Fig. 2 (c). Once this is set, no further regulation is necessary, provided that the pressure at the source of air supply does not falter. In order to get a gauge reading at this point, a constriction must be introduced between reducing valve C and tube F. A capillary tube is used for this purpose.

Flame

Very good results have been obtained with an arrangement similar to the one described by White (1). However, a copper coil for running water was placed around the chimney to prevent the heat from getting to the photocells (e).

It is important to know at all times that everything is running uniformly. No changes must take place in the air pressure coming in at *F*. Furthermore, it is very important to control the pressure of gas coming into the burner. This is done by a special reducing valve and gauge supplied in the Barclay instrument, Fig. 2 (*a*).

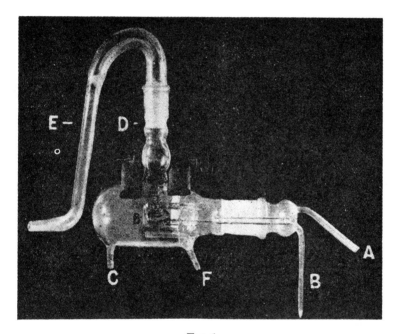

FIG. 1

They are very important, as the city gas pressure will vary from time to time, and there is no means of knowing this except by such a gauge in the line.

The original air supply usually operates between a minimum and a maximum level of pressure. When the pressure changes between these two points, there are correspondingly small changes in the reduced pressure between the supply and the outlets in the atomizer. By interposing another reducing valve (*d*) in the line, one can step down the pressure of the original supply, and then, by reducing it again before it enters the atomizer (*b*), one gets almost negligible changes in the outlet pressures.

Calibration

The calibration of a flame photometer may be done by either the direct or the indirect system of analysis, but the indirect method is much more accurate, particularly for the simpler instruments and for serum analysis. For urine samples, however, the direct system is usually satisfactory for clinical purposes. The advantage of the

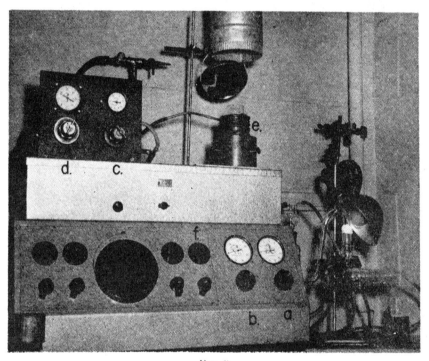

FIG. 2

direct method for urine is that the instrument will read over a much greater range of concentration. Urines can show from very low to very high concentrations of sodium and potassium. However, in serum, the physiological range is much narrower. Therefore, by employing lithium as a foreign ion, the potentiometer readings can be spread out to cover from 120 to 130 to 140 to 150 meq. of sodium per liter. This would correspond approximately to 11, 12, 13, and 14 p.p.m. in 1:250 dilution. Normally, sodium runs between 137 and 143 meq./l. The reason this particular range is used is that sodium usually decreases pathologically and seldom rises. Our lowest figure to date is 75 meq./l., and our highest figure is 170 meq./l. The amount of lithium used in both the standards and the unknowns is arbitrary. It is important to utilize as much of the potentiometer scale as is conveniently possible. By doing so, a minimum percentage of error per scale reading is obtained. The potentiometer readings are controlled by the amount of lithium used and also by turning the sensitivity potentiometer (f). In this preliminary setting up of the instrument, more lithium usually produces a shift in one direction and less lithium moves it in the other direction. Consequently, to change the potentiometer scale reading, one first turns the sensitivity knob. If this does not produce the desired effect, the lithium concentration must be changed up or down, as the case may be.

Potassium in serum is much lower than sodium, and therefore it should be diluted differently. The dilution for potassium is 1:100. Since potassium excites much less than sodium, less lithium per unit of dilution is used for potassium than for sodium. The standards used for potassium run between 2.5 meq./l. and 6 meq./l. Seldom do potassium levels go above 6 or below 2.5 meq./l. Here, again, the calibration is spread over most of the potentiometer for these concentrations. Three or four standard points are always run for both sodium and potassium prior to running unknowns. A standard is run after three or four unknowns to make sure that the calibration has not changed; with much fluctuation a standard must be checked after each unknown. The standards are plotted on graph paper against potentiometer readings.

Standard Solutions

1. Concentration of Stock, solutions:

STOCK SODIUM (DIRECT): 5.85 g. of sodium chloride per liter equals 100 meq. of sodium per liter.

STOCK POTASSIUM (DIRECT): 7.46 g. of potassium chloride per liter equals 100 meq. of potassium per liter.

STOCK SODIUM (INDIRECT): 254 mg. of sodium chloride per liter equals 100 p.p.m. of sodium.

STOCK POTASSIUM (INDIRECT): 191 mg. of potassium chloride per liter equals 100 p.p.m. of potassium.

STOCK LITHIUM SOLUTION: 12.5 g. of lithium sulfate per liter (each machine may require different concentrations of lithium to give the best results).

2. Working standards sodium (direct):

5 ml. of stock sodium direct to 1000 ml. equals 0.50 meq. of sodium per liter.

10 ml. of stock sodium direct to 1000 ml. equals 1.0 meq. of sodium per liter.

15 ml. of stock sodium direct to 1000 ml. equals 1.5 meq. of sodium per liter.

·20 ml. of stock sodium direct to 1000 ml. equals 2.0 meq. of sodium per liter.

Because of the fact that the sodium for direct determination is diluted 1:100, the latter concentrations become one hundred times as much, namely, 50, 100, 150, and 200 meq. of sodium per liter.

3. Working standards potassium (direct):

5 ml. of stock potassium direct to 1000 ml. equals 0.5 meq. of potassium per liter.

10 ml. of stock potassium direct to 1000 ml. equals 1.0 meq. of potassium per liter.

Because of the fact that the potassium for direct determination is diluted 1:100, the latter concentrations become one hundred times as much namely, 50 and 100 meq. of potassium per liter.

4. Working standards sodium (indirect):

110 ml. of stock sodium indirect plus 100 ml. of stock lithium to 1000 ml. equals 11 p.p.m.

120 ml. of stock sodium indirect plus 100 ml. of stock lithium to 1000 ml. equals 12 p.p.m.

130 ml. of stock sodium indirect plus 100 ml. of stock lithium to 1000 ml. equals 13 p.p.m.

140 ml. of stock sodium indirect plus 100 ml. of stock lithium to 1000 ml. equals 14 p.p.m.

5. Working standards potassium (indirect):

10 ml. of stock potassium indirect plus 30 ml. of stock lithium to 1000 ml. equals 1 p.p.m.

15 ml. of stock potassium indirect plus 30 ml. of stock lithium to 1000 ml. equals 1.5 p.p.m.

20 ml. of stock potassium indirect plus 30 ml. of stock lithium to 1000 ml. equals 2 p.p.m.

In making up the serum dilutions for sodium, 1 ml. is diluted to 250 ml. Since this represents one-fourth of a liter, only 25 ml. of stock lithium solution is used instead of the 100 ml. of lithium used in the working standards diluted to a liter. For potassium 1 ml. of serum is diluted to 100 ml. This will be one-tenth of a liter. Therefore, only 3 ml. of stock lithium is added, since 30 ml. is used per liter for the working standards.

Calculation

$$\text{Parts per million} \times \frac{\text{dilution}}{\text{equivalent weight}} = \text{Milliequivalents per liter}$$

Clinical Application

With the advent of flame photometry, a rapid, clinically accurate method is available for the determination of sodium and potassium. Previously, sodium determination was done infrequently and only on patients suspected of Addison's disease and a few other rare conditions, since it took two or three days by the regular chemical methods. Frequent electrolyte determinations as performed today were non-existent. It is of no clinical value to the physician to know what the sodium and potassium content is two or three days after the blood is drawn. It has been learned since that these values can change quite rapidly in many instances, such as after a major operation. Today, sodium and potassium determinations may be performed in a matter of minutes and the results made available to the physician very rapidly. This is very important, because corrective therapy may be started immediately. Disturbed electrolyte levels aggravate the patients' state in a striking manner. Today post-operative patients who are not taking food by mouth are checked regularly for sodium, potassium, chloride, and carbon dioxide content to see if the levels are being kept within the normal range. Therefore, if corrective therapy is necessary, it may be started immediately and unnecessary complications prevented.

Normal sodium values in serum should run about 140 ±3 meq./l.; potassium, 4.5 ±0.5 meq./l.; chloride, 100 ±3 meq./l., and carbon dioxide content, 28 ±1 meq./l. Since there must be corresponding anions to go with the cations, a quick check to see if the ions add up evenly on both sides is important. There are many different formulas for these computations, but the following very abbreviated one takes only a few seconds. If one considers that the average sodium value is 140 meq., the average potassium is 4.5 meq., the average chloride is 100 meq., and the average carbon dioxide content is 28 meq., one might see how far away the results of a patient are from these values. For example, typical results from a patient may be sodium 130 meq., potassium 4 meq., chloride 88 meq., and carbon dioxide content 30 meq. If one adds up the differences of the cations and the differences of the anions from the normal average, they should check each other within ±2. In this case, one would get −10 for the sodium (cation difference), −12 for the chloride, and +2 for the carbon dioxide, which would give a total anion difference of −10. Whenever the total cation difference equals the total anion difference within ±2, it may be considered fairly good correlation.

Since electrolyte determinations have become so popular, flame photometry is more and more in demand. In the larger hospitals, where adequately trained personnel is available, the problem of setting up and running the instrument is not too difficult. However, even in smaller hospitals, in the not-too-distant future, electrolyte determinations will be part of the routine.

The fundamental principles of flame photometry are basically the same, although the details vary in different instruments (2, 3). A more or less explicit set of directions comes with each apparatus. The precautions and improvements discussed will be found useful in the selection and care of any type of flame photometer.

BIBLIOGRAPHY

1. White, J. U., *Anal. Chem.* **24:** 394 (1952).
2. Natelson, S., *Am. J. Clin. Pathol.* **20:** 463 (1950).
3. Shukers, C. F., *Am. J. Clin. Pathol.* **22:** 606 (1952).

Thymol Turbidity

Submitted by: GEORGE R. KINGSLEY and G. GETCHELL, Veterans Administration
Center, Los Angeles, California.

Checked by: JOS KAHN,* Maimonides Hospital, Brooklyn, New York.
MARTIN RUBIN, Department of Chemistry, Chemo-Medical Institute,
Graduate School, Georgetown University, Washington, D.C.
CAPT. DAVID SELIGSON and MARJORIE KNOWLTON, Department of
Hepatic and Metabolic Disease, Walter Reed Army Medical
Center, Washington, D. C.

Authors: R. E. SHANK and C. L. HOAGLAND, *J. Biol. Chem.* **162**: 133 (1946).

Introduction

In certain diseases an abnormal alteration of the phospholipid-
protein complex of the serum beta globulin permits the precipitation
of a protein-thymolphospholipid complex upon the addition of a
buffered thymol solution to the serum. This test was first developed
as a visual turbidity test for liver function (1). The observation
was made that the material precipitated by the thymol reagent was
high in cholesterol and phosphorus. Ether extraction of the lipids
of serum positive to thymol reagent renders the serum negative to
this reagent (2). Electrophoretic analyses of sera positive to thymol
reagent before and after treatment with thymol reagent indicated
that removal of the thymol precipitate caused a decrease in the beta
globulin (3). The mobility of the thymol precipitate was also
similar to that of beta globulin. Other investigations indicated
that removal of either lipids or gamma globulins from the serum of
patients with infectious hepatitis reversed a positive thymol turbidity reaction (4). During early infectious hepatitis, when thymol
turbidity values are elevated, there was an increase in the electrophoretic beta globulin and plasma lipids, and later in the disease
there was an increase in the gamma globulin which was elevated as
long as the thymol turbidity reaction remained positive. Improve-

* Deceased.

ment of the stability and the standardization of the thymol reagent has been made by recrystallization of thymol (5), the use of alcohol (5), and buffering at pH 7.55 (6). A good reproducible method for turbidity standardization has been described (7).

Reagents

1. Folin and Ciocalteu phenol reagent (8): Add to a 1500-ml. Florence flask 100 g. of sodium tungstate ($Na_2WO_4 \cdot 2H_2O$), 25 g. of sodium molybdate ($Na_2MoO_4 \cdot 2H_2O$), 700 ml. of water, 50 ml. of 85% phosphoric acid, and 100 ml. of conc. hydrochloric acid. Reflux gently for 10 hours. Add 150 g. of lithium sulfate, 50 ml. of water, and a few drops of bromine. Boil the mixture for 15 minutes without the condenser under a hood to remove excess bromine. Cool, dilute to 1 l., and filter if necessary. The reagent should have a very pale yellow color with no greenish tint. Dilute with an *equal* portion of distilled water, and store in a glass-stoppered dark bottle.

2. 2.5 N NaOH.

3. Barbital buffer, (1): Dissolve 2.06 g. of sodium barbital (U.S.P.) and 2.75 g. of barbital (diethyl barbituric acid, U.S.P.) in distilled water and dilute to 1 l. Keep in refrigerator. Discard upon the appearance of any solid material.

4. Recrystallization of thymol: Add 100 g. of thymol (N.F.) to 100 ml. of 95% ethyl alcohol, and dissolve. Filter through Whatman No. 42 filter paper to remove insoluble material. Add 1 l. of cold distilled water to the filtrate. Mix. Let stand 20 minutes, and filter. Wash the crystals on filter twice with cold distilled water. Dry the crystals for 2 to 3 days in a dessicator over anhydrous calcium chloride to constant weight (m.p., 51.5° C.).

5. Thymol standard solution: Dissolve 50 mg. of recrystallized thymol in distilled water. Dilute to 1 l. in a volumetric flask.

6. Alcoholic 10% thymol standard reagent: Dissolve 10.000 g. of recrystallized thymol in 95% ethyl alcohol and dilute to 100 ml. in a volumetric flask.

7. Buffered alcoholic 0.1% thymol standard reagent. Add 1 ml. of alcoholic 10% thymol standard reagent to 80 ml. of barbital buffer in a 100-ml. volumetric flask, and shake vigorously until all oily droplets have disappeared. Dilute to volume with barbital buffer (1 ml. = 1 mg. of thymol). Adjust pH to 7.55.

STANDARDIZATION OF ALCOHOLIC THYMOL REAGENT: Measure 1, 2,

3, 4, and 5 ml. of standard thymol reagent, and 5 ml. of distilled water (blank) separately into six 50-ml. volumetric flasks. Dilute contents of all flasks to 25 ml. with distilled water. Add 4 ml. of 2.5 N NaOH. Add slowly, with shaking, 3 ml. of Folin-Ciocalteu reagent. Dilute to 50 ml. with distilled water. Mix. Let stand 15 minutes, and read within 5 minutes in photometer against per cent transmission set with blank using 620-mμ light transmission. Measure out 1, 2, 3, 4, and 5 ml. of a 5:100 dilution of the 0.1% alcoholic thymol reagent in the same manner to determine the thymol concentration of this reagent. This standardization should be carried out with each new batch of reagent. Determine K from the formula, mg. per 100 ml. $= K (2 - \log \%T)$.

Standardization of Turbidity Units: Reagents

1. 0.0962 N barium chloride: Dissolve 1.173 g. of barium chloride ($BaCl_2 \cdot 2H_2O$) in distilled water and dilute to 100 ml. (*Note:* In the original publication of turbidity standardization (7), the use of 0.0962 M barium chloride was intended, but it was printed as 0.0962 N. The latter concentration (which has become more widely used) obviously doubles the thymol turbidity units obtained.

2. 0.2 N sulfuric acid: Dilute approximately 6 ml. of conc. sulfuric acid to 1 l. Standardize against 0.1 N NaOH.

3. 20-unit thymol barium sulfate standard: Add 3 ml. of 0.0962 N barium chloride to a 100-ml. volumetric flask, and dilute to volume with 0.2 N sulfuric acid which has been chilled to 10° C. Adjust the final temperature of mixture to 20° C. before making final adjustment of volume to 100 ml.

STANDARDIZATION PROCEDURE: Place 0, 2, 4, 5, 8, and 10 ml. of 20-unit thymol barium sulfate standard in colorimeter cuvettes, and dilute each to 10 ml. at 10° C. Let tubes stand at room temperature (20–25° C.) for 30 minutes. Shake well before reading. Set 0 standard at 100 %/transmission with 650-mμ light transmission, and record readings of other standards at this setting (10 ml. standard = 20 thymol units). Calculate K from concentration of standards and transmission data, and prepare a table for conversion of per cent transmission to thymol turbidity units.

Procedure

Add 6 ml. of 0.1% alcoholic thymol reagent to each photometer cuvette. Add 0.1 ml. of serum from a 0.1-ml. differential pipette (if not differential, use a pipette calibrated to contain 0.1 ml., and wash out pipette with reagent). Add 0.1 ml. of distilled water to 6 ml. of 0.1% thymol reagent for blank. Mix. Let tubes stand 30 minutes at 25°C. Mix again, and immediately measure the transmittance of the unknown against the reagent blank set at 100% transmission with 650-mμ light transmission. Check standards should be run at frequent intervals with 2 and 8 ml. of the 20-unit thymol barium sulfate as described in Standardization Procedure.

Calculation

Concentration of units of thymol $= 88^*$ $(2 - \log \%T)$.
Thymol turbidity is measured in units per 0.1 ml. of serum.

Comments

Normal range: 0–5 units.

Abnormal range: Thymol turbidity units in serum are increased in liver disease during which normal liver cell metabolism is altered. This is noted especially in infectious hepatitis, and 40–50 units may be reached in this disease. This is one of the important tests used for investigating liver diseases and is valuable for following its course. Serial single determinations on patients with stable liver disease show daily variations not exceeding 10–15%, a replication suitable for clinical use.

Other conditions, such as Hodgkin's disease, infection with *Coccidioides immitis*, certain metallic poisonings, disseminated tuberculosis, lobar pneumonia, and subacute bacterial endocarditis, may be associated with elevated thymol turbidity units.

Precautions and Notes

Lipemic sera may give a false reaction and cause a non-specific increase in turbidity.

The turbidity standardization must be exact because of the nature of light absorption of turbid solutions. Each photometer must be carefully standardized and the standardization checked at frequent intervals. The use of copper sulfate (9) for standardization requires an additional standardization besides that outlined in this method and cannot be described here. Each individual photometer requires

---

* K for Coleman junior spectrophotometer cuvette 6-304B.

different concentrations of copper sulfate standards which must be established by turbidity standardization.

Recrystallized thymol must be weighed accurately on an analytical balance for preparation of alcoholic 10% thymol standard reagent. This aids in maintaining uniformity of the method, although many laboratories obtain suitable clinical results without this advantage.

Accurate adjustment of the pH of the buffered alcoholic 0.1% thymol standard reagent must be made. This condition is of critical importance.

The shortcomings of barium sulfate suspensions for standardization of thymol turbidity measurements are numerous, although use of a sufficient number of replicas and careful adherence to the prescribed conditions will give a fair approximation of a standard value. The use of copper sulfate also is objectionable because of the importance of the filter in determining its equivalence in filter-photometers. Work is in progress (Reinhold, J. G., Abstracts of American Chemical Society Meeting, Division of Biological Chemistry, Milwaukee, Wisconsin, page 25c, 1952) on the standardization of suspensions of colloidal pyrex glass. These are semi-permanent and have been found to have numerous advantages as compared with other standards.

BIBLIOGRAPHY

1. MacLagan, N. F., *Brit. J. Exptl. Pathol.* **25:** 234 (1944).
2. Recant, L., Chargaff, E., and Hanger, F., *Proc. Soc. Exptl. Biol. Med.* **60:** 245 (1945).
3. Cohen, P. P., and Thompson, F. L., *J. Lab. Clin. Med.* **32:** 475 (1947).
4. Kunkel, H. G., and Hoagland, C. L., *J. Clin. Invest.* **25:** 822 (1946).
5. Huerga, J. de la, and Popper, H., *J. Lab. Clin. Med.* **34:** 877 (1949).
6. Mateer, J. G., Baltz, J. I., Steele, H. H., Brouwer, S. W., and Colvert, J. R., *J. Am. Med. Assoc.* **133:** 909 (1947).
7. Shank, R. E., and Hoagland, C. L., *J. Biol. Chem.* **162:** 133 (1946).
8. Folin, O., and Ciocalteu, V., *J. Biol. Chem.* **73:** 627 (1929).
9. Ducci, H., *J. Lab. Clin. Med.* **32:** 1266 (1947).

Urea Nitrogen

Submitted by: OTTO SCHALES, Alton Ochsner Medical Foundation, New Orleans, Louisiana.

Checked by: ALBERT E. SOBEL, Jewish Hospital of Brooklyn, Brooklyn, New York.
JOSEPH BENOTTI, Pratt Diagnostic Clinic, New England Medical Center, Boston, Massachusetts.

Method: Direct Nesslerization Procedure.

Introduction

Urea nitrogen in blood can be determined accurately by incubating blood with urease and titrating the amount of ammonia formed, after it has been separated from the incubation mixture by distillation or aeration.   Many investigators felt that the separation of ammonia from the blood, after treatment with urease, was a somewhat inconvenient step, particularly if many tests had to be carried out simultaneously.   Numerous modifications have been published, therefore, which omit the removal of ammonia from the incubation mixture.   Instead, a protein-free filtrate is made, and its ammonia content is measured colorimetrically after addition of Nessler's reagent.

The submitter has compared a number of these "direct nesslerization" methods.   There is no doubt that the results obtained are not as accurate as "aeration method" results.   The method described below draws freely on the suggestions published by various authors.   It incorporates features which gave reasonably reliable results when compared with an aeration method.

The most disturbing observation made during these comparison studies concerns the difference in behavior between urease-treated blood and urease-treated urea standard solutions.   Urea standard solutions showed very little change in color intensity for about 30 minutes, once the colored complex had been formed after the addition of Nessler's reagent.   The color produced after nesslerization of urease-treated blood filtrates increased steadily until gross turbidity became visible after about 30 minutes.

It was found that comparison of the color intensity which existed 14–16 minutes after the addition of Nessler's reagent with the color intensity of hydrolyzed urea standard solution permitted the calculation of a result which agreed closely with macro aeration-titration experiments. The amount of ammonia found in the latter experiments, corrected for a blank, agreed with the calculated values, with a maximum error of less than 2%.

When readings were taken 10 minutes after the addition of Nessler's reagent, the results were about 10% too low, and readings taken 20 minutes after nesslerization gave results about 10% too high, in comparison with the aeration-titration procedure.

The gradual increase in color intensity of nesslerized blood or serum filtrates can be prevented by the addition of gluconate and persulfate to Nessler's solution (1). However, this stabilizing mixture has a bleaching effect also and consistently gave results 15–30% below those in aeration-titration method duplicates.

Urease was employed in the form of urease paper, but experiments with urease extracts prepared from jack bean powder gave identical results. In order to get reliable results, however, it is essential to adhere strictly to all other details outlined in the following procedure. It is not permissible, for example, to substitute other buffers for the buffer described here. This may be illustrated by the following observation. When, instead of the phosphate buffer used here, the phosphate buffer described by Sobel et al. (2) was used, there was no difficulty whatsoever in obtaining accurate results with the aeration method. However, considerably lower results were encountered invariably when a protein-free filtrate, prepared from an incubation mixture containing their buffer, was directly nesslerized.

Reagents

1. Phosphate buffer: Dissolve 6 g. of KH_2PO_4 and 2 g. of Na_2HPO_4 in a volumetric flask, and fill with water up to the 1000-ml. mark. Dilute this stock buffer solution 1:7 with water for use in the procedure. The dilute buffer solution has a pH of about 6.45, and the pH of the incubation mixture, after addition of blood, is about 6.8.

2. Urease paper after Folin and Svedberg (3): In a 200-ml. flask mix 30 g. of jack bean meal with 100 ml. of 30% alcohol (30 ml. of 95% alcohol diluted to 100 ml.) and 1 ml. of acetate buffer (containing 15 g. of cryst. sodium acetate and 1 ml. of glacial acetic acid in 100 ml.). Stopper tightly, and shake vigorously, for at least 5 minutes, and then shake less hard for 10 minutes. Centrifuge for about 10 minutes at 2000 r.p.m., and filter the supernatant solution through a large Whatman No. 50 filter paper, using only the filtrate obtained within 2 hours. Transfer the filtrate to a dry porcelain dish, and take it up at once on strips of Whatman No. 5 filter paper, 5 cm. wide, by drawing the strips through the urease solution. Hang the strips over two parallel threads about 15 cm. apart, in a place protected from air currents. As soon as the strips are dry, cut them into pieces about 1 × 2.5 cm., and store in the refrigerator in stoppered wide-mouth bottles.

3. 10% sodium tungstate solution.

4. 0.9 N H_2SO_4: Add 25 ml. of conc. H_2SO_4 to 975 ml. of water in a Florence flask. Cool under running tap water. Titrate with 1 N NaOH, using phenolphthalein as indicator, and adjust to the correct normality if necessary.

5. Urea nitrogen standard: Weigh 42.9 mg. of dry urea into a 100-ml. volumetric flask, dissolve in some water, and fill up to the 100-ml. mark with water. This solution contains 20 mg. of urea nitrogen per 100 ml. If abnormally high urea nitrogen values are expected, a more concentrated standard solution should be used for comparison.

6. Gum ghatti solution: Suspend 20 g. of soluble gum ghatti just below the surface of a liter of distilled water by means of a gauze bag. Let stand overnight, and filter through a clean towel.

7. Nessler's reagent after Koch and McMeekin (4): Dissolve 30 g. of potassium iodide in 20 ml. of water in a 500-ml. Erlenmeyer flask, and add 22.5 g. of iodine to the solution. Mix until dissolved, and then add 30 g. of pure metallic mercury. Shake the mixture well, keeping the solution cool by holding under running tap water from time to time, until the supernatant liquid has lost the yellow color of iodine. Pour off from the undissolved mercury, and test the fluid for the presence of excess iodine by adding a few drops to 5 ml. of a 1% starch solution in a test tube. If no blue color is obtained, add iodine solution (3 g. of potassium iodide, 2.25 g. of iodine, and 10 ml. of water) drop by drop to the decanted fluid until there is a faint excess of free iodine as determined by testing a few drops with starch solution. Dilute to 200 ml. with water, mix, and pour into 975 ml. of accurately prepared 10% NaOH solution. Mix, and store in the dark for several days before use, permitting any precipitate to settle out. Avoid stirring up the sediment when removing part of the clear supernatant fluid from the storage bottle.

Procedure

To 7 ml. of phosphate buffer add 1 ml. of oxalated blood and 1 piece of urease paper. Simultaneously, set up a blank (substituting 1 ml. of water for blood) and a standard (substituting 1 ml. of urea solution containing 20 mg. of urea nitrogen per 100 ml.). Keep the three incubation mixtures at room temperature (22–26° C.) for 30 minutes or at 37° C. for 15–20 minutes. Mix the contents of each flask at intervals during the incubation. At the end of the incubation period, add 1 ml. of 10% sodium tungstate solution and 1 ml. of 0.9 N H_2SO_4 to each flask. Let stand for 10 minutes, then centrifuge (2000 r.p.m., International centrifuge, size 1) for 10 minutes.

Into a colorimeter tube place 2 ml. of supernatant fluid, 8 ml. of water, 1 drop of gum ghatti, and 4 ml. of Nessler's solution.

Mix by inversion. Set the blank to read 100% transmittancy at 490 mμ (a Lumetron colorimeter, Model 402-E, was used for this work), and determine the transmittancy of the unknown and standard solutions 14–16 minutes after the addition of Nessler's reagent.

Calculation

The concentration of urea nitrogen in the test solution (blood) is calculated by comparing the extinction (2 − log transmittancy) of the unknown with that of the standard solution, which contained 20 mg. of urea nitrogen per 100 ml. In other words,

Urea nitrogen in unknown (mg. per 100 ml.) =

$$\frac{\text{Extinction of unknown}}{\text{Extinction of standard}} \times 20$$

Normal Values

Normal values for urea nitrogen in blood are 10–18 mg. in 100 ml.

Pathological Values

The most common cause for increased blood urea nitrogen is inadequate excretion, usually due to kidney disease or urinary obstruction. Increased blood urea nitrogen in acute nephritis may vary from 25–160 mg. per 100 ml. Urea retention occurs with extensive parenchymatous destruction of the kidneys as in pyelonephritis, advanced nephrosclerosis, renal tuberculosis, renal cortical necrosis, malignancy, suppuration and chronic gout. Renal conditions producing anuria or marked oliguria as in carbon tetrachloride poisoning, post-operative urinary suppression, mercuric chloride poisoning, and advanced myocardial failure result in the retention of urea in the blood.

Decreased blood urea nitrogen is encountered in conditions associated with acute hepatic insufficiency and often in normal pregnancy.

Comments

In comparative studies of the nessierization and aeration procedures there may be a slight tendency toward higher results using the Nesslerization method. The recovery of known amounts of urea added to blood serum was excellent when the nesslerization method was employed.

BIBLIOGRAPHY
1. Gentzkow, C. F., *J. Biol. Chem.* **143:** 531 (1942).
2. Sobel, A. E., Mayer, A. M., and Gottfried, S. P., *J. Biol. Chem.* **156:** 355 (1944).
3. Folin, O., and Svedberg, A., *J. Biol. Chem.* **88:** 81 (1930).
4. Koch, F. C., and McMeekin, T. L., *J. Am. Chem. Soc.* **46:** 2066 (1924).

Uric Acid

Submitted by: SAMUEL NATELSON, Rockford Memorial Hospital, Rockford, Illinois.

Checked by: MARGARET KASER, Veterans Administration Center, Wood, Wisconsin.

Author: H. BROWN, *J. Biol. Chem.* **158:** 601 (1945).

Introduction

Most methods for the estimation of uric acid depend upon the ease with which uric acid is oxidized in either acid or alkaline media. In acid medium the chief products of the action of mild oxidizing agents are alloxan and urea as first shown by Brugnatelli (14). In alkaline medium the chief products are allantoin and CO_2 (85).

Uric acid has been separated in both acid and alkaline media by precipitation of the silver (31), Mg (36), NH_4 (11), cuprous (38), and cupric (79) salts, or mixtures of these salts. With low concentrations, as in blood serum, the solubility of the salts becomes appreciable and precipitation methods introduce serious error (67). For urine with larger concentrations of uric acid, the precipitation methods are satisfactory. Specificity claimed for the precipitation methods is doubtful, since other purines precipitate as these salts and other reducing substances come down with the precipitate (8).

Benedict and Behre (5), Christman and Ravwitsch (19), and Keighley and Borsook (50) use arsenotungstic acid instead of the phosphotungstic acid. The intensity of the blue color developed with the reagent of Folin or Benedict is usually estimated colorimetrically, as described above, or titrimetrically by discharging it as with chlorine water (82) or $K_3Fe(CN)_6$ (48).

Alkaline oxidation to allantoin has been extensively used. For $K_3Fe(CN)_6$, 2 moles of the reagent are required for 1 mole of uric acid (32). Colorimetric procedures based on this method have also been employed (58, 81). Potentiometric measurements have been used after oxidation with $K_3Fe(CN)_6$ (2, 4). Uranyl acetate in alkaline medium also converts uric acid to allantoin and has been used for its estimation (29, 51).

Oxidation by numerous oxidizing agents, usually after precipitation as the insoluble urate salt, has also found application. Iodine (7, 20, 22, 38), dichromate (44), and permanganate (68) have been used. Dichromate and permanganate yield CO_2 and water as end products of oxidation. Two moles of chloramine will oxidize 1 mole of uric acid and has been used for analytical purposes (83). The conversion of uric acid to ammonium purpurate (murexide) after oxidation with nitric acid and treatment with ammonia has been used qualitatively (28). This reaction is given by other purines. Butyl amine has been substituted for ammonia to make the reaction more sensitive (57).

Other reagents which have been used for the production of a color with uric acid are p-amino phenol or p-N-methyl amino phenol in the presence of $K_2S_2O_8$; to produce a yellow color (62) and 2,6-dichloroquinone chloroimide with 1% $AgNO_3$ to produce a red color (25). Hydrolysis of uric acid to urea and estimation of the urea so produced has also been employed for quantitative uric acid estimation (37).

In order to achieve specificity, many investigators (9, 10, 15, 55, 66) resort to destruction of uric acid by the enzyme uricase and determination of the residual reducing substance to be subtracted from the total reducing substance.

Uric acid *per se* exhibits an absorption maximum in the ultraviolet and has been determined directly in the spectrograph (54)

at 270–280 mμ and with the spectrophotometer (24) at 290 mμ both
before and after the action of uricase (49). Other purines exhibit
maxima at the same wavelength.

Partial calcination of uric acid gives a blue fluorescent substance
(41), but this has been used only for identification purposes. Neph-
elometric measurement of colloidally precipitated uric acid has also
found application (75).

The method described is an alkaline oxidation applied directly
to a protein-free serum filtrate. It is the method of Folin (33) as
modified by Brown (13). The oxidizing agent is phosphotungstic
acid in the presence of NaCN "buffered" by urea.

Reagents

1. Uric acid reagent (phosphotungstic acid): Into a 500-ml. round-
bottomed flask, which has been cleaned with dichromate-sulfuric
acid cleaning solution and fitted with a ground-glass joint, place
50 g. of sodium tungstate ($Na_2WO_4 \cdot 2H_2O$) and 10 g. of anhydrous
disodium phosphate (or 18.9 g. of $Na_2HPO_4 \cdot 7H_2O$). Now add
150 ml. of water, and warm the flask until complete solution has
taken place. Add 12.5 ml. of concentrated sulfuric acid (sp. gr.
1.84) to 50 ml. of water. When cool, add the sulfuric acid solution
to the tungstate solution. Fit a condenser cleaned with dichromate-
sulfuric acid to the ground joint, and reflux the mixture for 1 hour.
Cool, transfer with rinsing to a 500-ml. volumetric flask, and dilute
to mark. The reagent is stable indefinitely and should be practically colorless. If it becomes blue, or if the blank determination
develops a high degree of color, add a drop of bromine and boil the
solution to remove excess bromine.

2. Sodium cyanide solution, 12% (poison): Dissolve 12 g. of NaCN
in water, and dilute to 100 ml. Keep in refrigerator in a dark
bottle with a ground-glass stopper. Date the bottle, and do not
use the solution after it is one month old.

3. Urea solution, 50%: Dissolve 50 g. of urea in water, and make
up to 100 ml. This reagent is stable at room temperature. Urea
will crystallize out if placed in the refrigerator.

4. Urea cyanide solution: Just before use, mix equal volumes of
the 50% urea solution and the 12% sodium cyanide solution in a
glass-stoppered graduated cylinder.

5. Uric acid stock standard, 100 μg./ml.: Weigh out 100 mg. of uric acid, and transfer to a 1-l. volumetric flask. Dissolve 0.3 g. of lithium carbonate in 100 ml. of water, and filter. Heat the lithium carbonate solution to 60° C., and pour on to the uric acid. Shake until all the uric acid dissolves (the solution usually remains slightly turbid). Cool the flask under running water. Add 20 ml. of 40% formaldehyde (formalin). Dilute to about 500 ml., and add 15 ml. of normal sulfuric acid. Mix, dilute to the mark, and transfer to a dark-brown bottle. The solution will now be clear. Keep in a cool, dark place (refrigerator). (Normal H_2SO_4 is obtained by diluting concentrated acid 1:36).

6. *Dilute uric acid working standard, 2 µg./ml.:* Dilute the uric acid stock standard (100 µg./ml.) 1:50 by diluting 1 ml. to 50 ml. in a volumetric flask. Prepare fresh once a week. Keep in the refrigerator.

7. *Tungstic acid solution:*

(a) *0.15 N H_2SO_4:* Dilute 8.3 ml. of conc. H_2SO_4 (sp. gr. 1.84) to 2 liters.

(b) *2.2% sodium tungstate:* Dissolve 22 g. of $Na_2WO_4 \cdot 2H_2O$ in water and dilute to 1 liter.

Mix equal parts of (a) and (b) on the day of the test.

Procedure

Mix 1 vol. of serum with 19 vol. of tungstic acid solution. Allow the mixture to stand for 3 minutes, and then centrifuge for 10 minutes at 1500 r.p.m. in a centrifuge equivalent to the International centrifuge No. 1, or filter the mixture.

1. *Blank:* Mix well 2 ml. of water and 4 ml. of urea-cyanide solution in a test tube with a mark at 10 ml. (Kimble No. 45071). Add 1.0 ml. of uric acid reagent, and mix well. Allow to stand 25 minutes at 25° C., and dilute to 10 ml. Use this solution to set the galvanometer of the instrument to zero density or 100% transmittance at 680 mµ in the spectrophotometer when reading the unknown and standards.

2. *Unknown:* To 1.0 ml. of the supernatant or filtrate add 1.0 ml. of water and 4 ml. of the urea-cyanide solution in a test tube with a mark at 10 ml. (Kimble No. 45071). Mix well. Add 1.0 ml. of uric acid reagent. Mix well. Place in a 25°C. bath, and allow to stand for 25 minutes. Dilute to mark, or add 3.0 ml. water and mix by inversion. Read at 680 mµ. in the spectrophotometer.

3. *Standard:* Mix well 1 ml. of dilute standard (2 µg./ml.), 1 ml.

of water, and 4 ml. of urea-cyanide solution. Now add 1.0 ml. of uric acid reagent. Mix well, and allow to stand 25 minutes at 25° C. Dilute to 10 ml., and read as for the unknown.

4. Recovery: Add 0.5 ml. of tungstic acid filtrate to 0.5 ml. of uric acid standard (2 μg./ml.). Now add 1 ml. of water, 4 ml. of urea-cyanide solution, and 1.0 ml. of uric acid reagent. Proceed as for the unknown.

Calculation

Results are estimated by reference to a calibration curve. This calibration curve is checked with each set of determinations by running the 2 μg./ml. standard as described above (equivalent to 4 mg. per 100 ml. of uric acid in serum). If the standard deviates appreciably from the standard curve, a new standard curve should be prepared. Usually such deviation signifies deterioration of the dilute standard, contamination of the uric acid reagent, or deterioration of the sodium cyanide solution. If a standard, freshly diluted from stock, gives unsatisfactory results, it is best to prepare all reagents before making the new standard curve. The standard curve will approximately follow Beer's law in concentrations less than 4 μg. in the reaction tube (equivalent to 8 mg. per 100 ml. in serum).

1. Standard curve: 0.5, 1.0, 2.0, 3.0, 4.0, 6.0, and 8.0 μg. of uric acid are introduced into 10-ml. reaction tubes, and the volume in each tube is made up to 2 ml. The reading is obtained on the instrument used by adding 4 ml. of the urea-cyanide solution and 1.0 ml. of uric acid reagent, proceeding as for the unknown.

Using the 2 μg./ml. dilute uric acid standard, 0.25, 0.50, 1.0, 1.5, and 2.0 ml. are introduced into the reaction tubes for 0.5, 1.0, 2.0, 3.0, and 4.0 μg., respectively. For 6 and 8 μg., 1.5 and 2.0 ml. of the stock standard diluted 1:25 (4 μg./ml.) are used, respectively.

Density readings vs. micrograms used or serum concentrations are plotted on ordinary graph paper. If per cent transmission readings are made, results are plotted on semilog graph paper. The concentration in the serum analyzed, expressed in milligrams per 100 ml., is twice the number of micrograms read off the chart. For example, 2 μg. is equivalent to 4 mg. per 100 ml.

2. Calculation of recovery: From the standard curve, the calculation of the percentage recovered is represented by the formula:

% uric acid recovered

= (Total μg. found − μg. added from serum) × 100

EXAMPLE: The serum used yielded a value of 4.8 mg. per 100 ml. Therefore 0.5 ml. of filtrate contained 1.2 μg., which is the amount added to the tube. One microgram was added from the dilute standard (0.5 ml.). If the amount found in the tube is 2.15 μg., then the percentage recovered is (2.15 − 1.2) 100, or 95% recovered.

Notes on the Procedure

If urine is to be analyzed, dilute the urine 1:10, and then proceed as for serum.

A 1:10 tungstic acid filtrate may be prepared by adding 8 ml. of N/12 sulfuric acid to 1 ml. of serum and then adding 1 ml. of 10% sodium tungstate. In this case 0.5 ml. of filtrate is used, to which is added 1.5 ml. of water before the urea cyanide and uric acid reagent are added.

If 0.1 ml. of serum is to be analyzed, then 1.9 ml. of tungstic acid solution is added, mixed, and centrifuged. A 1-ml. aliquot is analyzed as described.

This procedure is described for the 1.6–cm.light path as in the Coleman spectrophotometer. For other instruments with shorter light path, higher color intensity will be obtained by adding 1 ml. of filtrate to 1.0 ml. of water, followed by 2 ml. of urea cyanide reagent and 0.5 ml. of uric reagent, allowing it to stand for 25 minutes at 25° C. and reading the color without dilution. In the Klett-Summerson colorimeter, a No. 66 (red) filter is used.

Sources of Error

In the precipitation of proteins with tungstic acid, some of the uric acid is precipitated. The phosphotungstic acid reagent is not specific for uric acid and will be reduced by ferrous salts, glutathione, phenols, ascorbic acid, glucose, tyrosine, tryptophan, cystine, and cysteine (9). Folin claimed, however, that, within the time allotted for the development of the color, substances like phenols and glucose will not interfere at room temperature. Reducing sulfur compounds are present in relatively large quantities in the erythrocytes, and hence it is recommended that the procedure be carried out on serum or plasma (21). The presence of a substance in the red cells which inhibits the development of the color has been demonstrated (78).

Time, temperature, and concentration of reagents must be held constant for blanks, standards, recoveries, and unknowns in order to obtain a uniform rate of color development. In the method described above, these factors have been kept constant. Final dilution slows down the development of color and permits a suitable time interval for reading. Color development at 25 minutes is approximately 95% of the color development at the end of an hour.

The major difficulty with the method is obtaining satisfactory recoveries (33, 34, 35, 36, 67). In our hands, the original method of Brown yielded recoveries of 60–85% of added uric acid; the larger the amount of uric acid, the lower was the percentage recovered when a calibration curve was not used. Mean recovery with the procedure described above on thirty-seven samples ranged from 91 to 106% of the uric acid added, with the mean at 95% and a standard deviation of ±3 from the mean recovery.

Poor recovery in uric acid methods as reported by numerous investigators apparently stem from the fact that the development of the color does not follow Beer's law. In general, at lower concentrations a curve approximating a straight line is obtained, which curves over rather sharply as the concentration is increased. If a standard curve is used for calculation, recoveries seem to be excellent. The reading of the color at the peak absorption will increase sensitivity and tend to increase specificity (Fig. 1).

If the tungstic acid is allowed to stand for more than 24 hours before use, a white precipitate of tungstic oxide will form in the blanks and standards on standing in the water bath. If this is centrifuged off, the supernatant will contain all the color and may be read. It is best to prepare the tungstic acid on the day of the test.

Normal Level of Uric Acid in Body Fluids

At normal pH the uric acid level in the plasma is approximately twice the concentration of that in the red cells (87). The distribution of uric acid between cells and plasma apparently depends upon the bicarbonate concentration and the pH of the blood (77). Thus, it is not surprising that whole blood levels are substantially lower than serum or plasma levels. The whole blood uric acid level will be markedly influenced by the hematocrit value. Since the hematocrit value varies widely in health and disease, and since the red cells contribute most of the non-specific substances, it is best to perform the analysis on serum or plasma. With oxalated blood, excessive amounts of oxalate may cause turbidity when the uric acid reagent is added to plasma filtrates.

Most of the data on normal subjects have, unfortunately, been

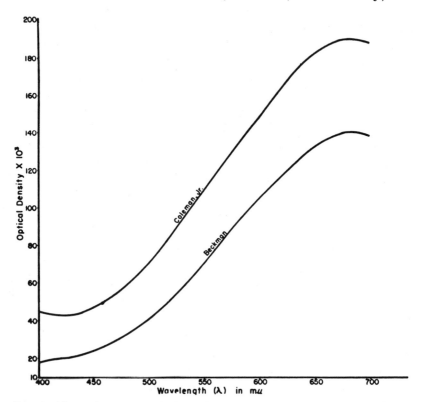

FIG. 1 Absorption curve of the color obtained by the method described. The solution contains 2 μg. of uric acid, and its depth is 1 cm. for the Beckman spectrophotometer and 1.6 cm. for the Coleman junior spectrophotometer.

listed for whole blood. Table I lists the normal range found by several investigators. Comparison should be made in accordance with the fluid analyzed. Blood from females apparently contains less uric acid than that from males, which should also be taken into account. Using the method described above on fifty-one apparently normal adults (age group, 19–45 years), both male and female, values were obtained ranging from 2.4 to 5.9 mg. per 100 ml. of

URIC ACID 131

uric acid in serum, with a mean value of 4.3. This is to be compared with the figures listed in Table I.

The uric acid level in spinal fluid is low (6, 40, 65) and has been reported as normally equal to approximately 5% of the blood level in good health and as high as 22% of the blood value in severe

TABLE I

URIC ACID LEVELS IN WHOLE BLOOD, PLASMA, AND SERUM IN APPARENTLY NORMAL INDIVIDUALS

Author	Method	Sample	Sex	Range	Mean value
Jacobson (46)	Folin	Plasma	M + F	2–6.9	4.2
Brøhner-Mortenson (12)	Flotow	Plasma	M + F	4.6–8.8	—
Bulger and Johns (15)	Uricase	Plasma	F	2–6	3.5
Bulger and Johns (15)	Uricase	Plasma	M	2–6	4.4
Leone and Manzi (55)	Uricase	Serum	M + F	5–6	—
Folin (33)	Folin	Whole blood	M + F	1.3–3.0	2.5
Blauch and Koch (9)	Uricase	Whole blood	M + F	1.04–3.83	2.0
Blauch and Koch (9)	Folin	Whole blood	M + F	1.82–4.6	3.0
Brown (13)	Folin	Whole blood	M	2.22–3.45	—
			F	1.88–2.90	—
Brown (13)	Uricase	Whole blood	M	20.5–3.10	—
			F	1.70–2.80	—
Block and Geib (10)	Uricase	Whole blood	M + F	2.35–4.42	—
Natelson and Kaser (Present study of 51 adults)	Brown	Serum	M + F	2.4–5.9	4.3

disease. The percentage seems to increase with the white cell count, with the highest values found in terminal conditions.

Intermittent palmar sweat contains approximately 0.8 mg. per 100 ml., while in profuse sweat uric acid levels are very low (56).

The normal adult excretes 0.1–2 g. of uric acid daily in the urine, depending upon the diet. The highest value has been reported on a high purine diet. On a normal mixed diet, 0.3–0.9 g. will be excreted (17, 39, 63). In normal individuals the uric acid excretion will be about the same whether the protein is derived from a low purine diet or a mixed diet with moderate amounts of purines (59, 88).

The uric acid content of the stool will vary somewhat with the diet and the extent to which undigested food particles are present. However, when liquid stools, induced in normal individuals, were analyzed, they were found to contain a mean level of 8.8 mg. per 100 ml. of stool (46).

Conditions under Which the Level of Uric Acid Is Altered

Man seems to form uric acid from the pyrimidines and the purines of the nucleic acids (3, 80). Evidence has also been presented that amino acid or protein nitrogen will appear in the urine as uric acid, (74), since uric acid will be excreted in excess of the amount ingested on a low purine diet (23, 53). It is not surprising, therefore, to find increased uric acid levels in the plasma and urine in those conditions where excessive cell breakdown and catabolism of nucleic acid occur. Increases have been observed in fatal poisoning with methyl alcohol (64) and chloroform (72). In the acute stages of infectious diseases such as pneumonia (84), increased uric acid levels have been reported. Excessive exposure to X-rays and radioactive irradiation will cause increases in serum uric acid levels (27). In the first few days after birth, when massive destruction of erythrocytes is taking place, and during the period of "physiological jaundice," increases in the urinary output of uric acid in infants have been reported (52, 69). In severe uremia (43), congestive heart failure, atherosclerosis, and essential hypertension, increased levels of uric acid are found in excess of that attributable to reduced kidney function (30). In eclampsia, or toxemia of pregnancy, elevated uric acid levels are often found associated with reduced urea levels (18).

In multiple myeloma, increases are out of proportion to the increase in urea nitrogen (73). In leukemia, where the white cell count may be enormous, marked increases in uric acid levels are observed (34). In polycythemia vera, increases in uric acid levels are also noted (45). In severe disease and in terminal states increases in spinal fluid uric acid levels have been reported (6). Increased uric acid levels are found toward the end of pregnancy, during and just after labor (42).

Most commonly, increases in uric acid levels are found to be associated with nitrogen retention and increased urea, creatinine, and other non-protein constituents (26, 47, 60). This must often be interpreted as another indication of decreased kidney function. Increased uric acid levels in gout have been extensively studied (46,76). Lowered uric acid blood levels have been reported in acromegaly (70) and polyarthritis (12). Under the influence of certain drugs such as benemid (61), colchicine (86), atophan (cinchophen), novatophan (27, 71), salicylates (27), and piperazine (16), uric acid levels are reported to be lowered. In acute yellow liver atrophy, blood uric acid levels are greatly reduced (64). In terminal nephritis some reduction of uric acid from previously high levels has also been noted (26). Variation of non-ultrafilterable (bound) uric acid in normal subjects and patients with miscellaneous pathologic conditions has been studied also (1).

BIBLIOGRAPHY

1. Adlersberg, D., Grishman, E., and Sobotka, H., *Arch. Internal. Med.* **70**: 101 (1942).
2. Barnard, R. D., *J. Lab. Clin. Med.* **16**: 1101 (1931).
3. Barnes, F. W., Jr., and Schoenheimer, R., *J. Biol. Chem.* **151**: 123 (1943).
4. Beccari, E., *Boll. soc. ital. biol. Sper.* **15**: 372 (1940).
5. Benedict, S. R., and Behre, J., *J. Biol. Chem.* **92**: 161 (1931).
6. Bernhard, A., *J. Lab. Clin. Med.* **9**: 753 (1924).
7. Birbraer, M. I., *Lab. Prakt. (U.S.S.R.)* No. 5, 39 (1937).
8. Blankenstein, A., *Biochem. Z.* **238**: 461 (1931).
9. Blauch, M. B., and Koch, F. C., *J. Biol. Chem.* **130**: 443 (1939).
10. Block, W. D., and Geib, N. C., *J. Biol. Chem.* **168**: 747 (1947).
11. Boivin, A., *Bull. soc. chim. biol.* **9**: 149 (1927).
12. Brøhner-Mortensen, K., *Acta Med. Scand.* **96**: 438 (1938); **99**: 538 (1939).
13. Brown, H., *J. Biol. Chem.* **158**: 601 (1945).
14. Brugnatelli, A., *Phil. Mag.* **52**: 30 (1818); *Ann. chim. et phys.* **8**: 201 (1817).
15. Bulger, H. A., and Johns, H. E., *J. Biol. Chem.* **140**: 427 (1941).
16. Burger, M., *Naunyn-Schmiedeberg's Arch. exptl. Pathol. Pharmakol.* **87**: 392 (1920).
17. Burian, R., and Schur, H., *Pflüger's Arch. ges. Physiol.* **87**: 239 (1910).
18. Cadden, J. F., and Stander, H. J., *Am. J. Obstet. Gynecol.* **37**: 37 (1939).
19. Christman, A. A., and Ravwitsch, S., *J. Biol. Chem.* **95**: 115 (1932).
20. Claudius, M., *Beretn. 18th Skand. Naturforskermøde* 225 (1929).
21. Coste, F., and Grigaut, A., *Presse méd.* **44**: 229 (1936).
22. Danet, R., *J. pharm. chim.* **6**: 405 (1927); *Bull. biologistes pharm.* page 64 (1936). *Chimie et industrie* **37**: 1077 (1936).
23. Denis, W., *J. Biol. Chem.* **23**: 147 (1915).
24. Eisenbrand, J., *Arch. Pharm.* **268**: 520 (1930).
25. Fearon, W. R., *Biochem. J.* **38**: 399 (1944).
26. Feinblatt, H. M., *Med. J. and Record* **67**: 737 (1923); *Arch. Internal Med.* **31**: 758 (1923).

134 STANDARD METHODS OF CLINICAL CHEMISTRY

27. Fine, M. S., and Chase, A. F., *J. Pharmacol. Exptl. Therap.* **6:** 219 (1914–15); *J. Biol. Chem.* **21:** 371 (1915).
28. Fischer, E., *Ber. deut. chem. Ges.* **30:** 2226 (1897).
29. Fischer, P., and Hupmann, G., *Süddeut. Apoth. Ztg.* **72:** 2 (1932).
30. Fishberg, A. M., *Arch. Internal Med.* **34:** 503 (1924).
31. Fleury, P., and Genevois, P., *J. Pharm. Chim.* [8]**4:** 102, 201 (1926).
32. Flotow, L., *Biochem. Z.* **176:** 178 (1926).
33. Folin, O., *J. Biol. Chem.* **86:** 179 (1930); **101:** 111 (933); **106:** 311 (1934).
34. Folin, O., and Denis, W., *Arch. Internal Med.* **16:** 33 (1915).
35. Folin, O., Berglund, H., and Derick, C., *J. Biol. Chem.* **60:** 361 (1924).
36. Folin, O., and Marenzi, A. D., *J. Biol. Chem.* **83:** 109 (1929).
37. Fosse, R., Brunel, A., and de Graveve, P., *Compt. rend.* **190:** 693 (1930).
38. Ganassini, D., *Arch. ist. biochim. ital.* **1:** 167 (1929); **2:** 505 (1930).
39. Garry, R. C., *J. Physiol.* **62:** 364 (1926–27).
40. Giordano, G. G., *Acta Neurol. (Naples)* **5:** 193–9 (1950).
41. Hadjioloff, A., and Kresteff, T., *Compt. rend. soc. biol.* **106:** 663 (1931).
42. Harding, V. J., Allin, K. D., and Van Wyck, H. B., *J. Obstet. Gynaecol. Brit. Empire* **31:** 594 (1924).
43. Holbrook, W. P., and Haskins, H. D., *J. Lab. Clin. Med.* **12:** 11 (1926).
44. Ionescu, M., and Popesco, A., *Bull. soc. chim. biol.* **21:** 264 (1939).
45. Isaacs, R., *Arch. Internal. Med.* **31:** 289 (1923).
46. Jacobson, B. M., *Ann. Internal. Med.,* **11:** 1277 (1938).
47. Johnston, C., *J. Clin. Invest.* **9:** 555 (1931).
48. Kallos, J., *Orvosi Hetilap.* **83:** 540 (1939).
49. Kalckar, H. M., and Shafran, J., *J. Biol. Chem.* **167:** 429 (1947).
50. Keighley, G., and Borsook, H., *J. Lab. Clin. Med.* **19:** 650 (1934).
51. Kern, A., and Strausky, E., *Biochem. Z.* **290:** 419 (1937).
52. Kingsbury, F. B., and Sedgwick, S. P., *J. Biol. Chem.* **31:** 261 (1917).
53. Kollmann, G., *Biochem. Z.* **123:** 235 (1921).
54. Krupski, A., and Almasy, F., *Naturwissenschaften* **19:** 461 (1931).
55. Leone, E., and Manzi, G., *Boll. soc. ital. biol. sper.* **23:** 823 (1947).
56. Lobitz, W. C., and Mason, H. L., *Arch. Dermatol. Syphilol.* **57:** 387, 907 (1948).
57. Martini, A., *Pub. inst. invest. microquim. Univ. nacl. litoral (Rosario, Arg)* **1:** 61 (1937).
58. Montequi, F., *Anales soc. españ. fis. quim.* **29:** 264 (1931).
59. voñ Moraczewski, W., Grzycki, S., Jankowski, H., and Sliwinski, R., *Klin. Wochschr.* **12:** 738 (1933).
60. Myers, V. C., and Fine, M. S., *J. Biol. Chem.* **37:** 239 (1919).
61. Pascale, L. R., Dubin, A., and Hoffman, W. S., *J. Am. Med. Assoc.* **149 :** 1188 (1952).
62. Pitarelli, E., *Arch. farmacol. sper.* **1:** 167 (1929).
63. Plentl, A. A., and Schoenheimer, R., *J. Biol. Chem.* **153:** 203 (1944).
64. Rabinowitch, I. M., *Arch. Internal. Med.* **29:** 821 (1922); *J. Biol. Chem.* **83:** 333 (1929).
65. Reiche, F. Z., *Klin. Med.* **125:** 565 (1933).
66. Schaffer, N. K., *J. Biol. Chem.* **153:** 163 (1944).

67. Scheiner, E., *Biochem. Z.* **205**: 245 (1929).
68. Schewket, O., *Biochem. Z.* **224**: 322 (1930).
69. Schloss, O. M., and Crawford, J. L., *Am. J. Diseases Children* **1**: 203 (1911).
70. Schmidt, G., *Z. ges. exptl. Med.* **94**: 76 (1934).
71. Smith, C. A., and Hawk, P. B., *Arch. Internal. Med.* **15**: 181 (1915).
72. Stander, H. J., *Bull. Johns Hopkins Hosp.* **35**: 46 (1924).
73. Stewart, A., and Weber, F. P., *Quart. J. Med.* **7**: 211 (1938).
74. Stetten, D., *J. Mt. Sinai Hosp. N. Y.* **17**: 149 (1950).
75. Taillandier, M., and Leroy, D., *Compt. rend. soc. biol.* **97**: 706 (1927).
76. Talbott, J. H., and Coombs, F. S., *J. Am. Med. Assoc.* **110**: 1977 (1938).
77. Talbott, J. H., and Sherman, J. M., *J. Clin. Invest.* **15**: 457 (1936).
78. Tastaldi, H., and Tastaldi, E., *Anais fac. farm. e odontol univ. São Paulo* **3**: 41–95 (1942–43).
79. Tixier, L., *Bull. sci. pharmacol.* **36**: 77 (1929).
80. Usseglio, G., and Amerio, A., *Minerva med.* **40**: II, 181 (1949).
81. Van Assenraad, J. D. B.H., *Pharm. Tijdschr. Nederland.-Indië* **6**: 65 (1929).
82. Vladesco, R., *Bull. soc. chim. biol.* **10**: 602 (1928).
83. Vstecka, Lad., *Časopis Československ. Lékárnictva* **15**: 51 (1935).
84. Wells, C. W., *Arch. Internal. Med.* **26**: 443 (1920).
85. Wohler, F., and Liebig, J., *Ann. Chemie Justus Liebigs* **26**: 285 (1838).
86. Wolfson, W. Q., and Cohn, C., 241, Proceedings of the First Clinical ACTH Conference, p. 241, Mote, J. R., Blakiston, Pa., 1950.
87. Wu, H., *J. Biol. Chem.* **51**: 21 (1921).
88. Young, E. G., Conway, C. F., and Crandall, W. A., *Biochem. J.* **32**: 1138 (1938).

Author Index

Numbers in parentheses are reference numbers. They are included to assist the reader to locate references in which the authors' names are not listed. Italic numbers indicate pages on which references are listed.

A

Adlersberg, D., 133 (1), *133*
Alexander, E., 72 (4), *74*
Allin, K. D., 132 (42), *134*
Almasy, F., 124 (54), *134*
Alper, C., 72 (4), 73 (5, 6, 7), *74*
Amerio, A., 132 (80), *135*
Appelyard, J., 82 (7), *83*
Archibald, R. M., 94 (6), *97*
Armstrong, A. R., *75*

B

Baltz, J. I., 114 (6), *117*
Bardawill, C. J., 95, *97*
Barnard, R. D., 124 (2), *133*
Barnes, B. A., 95 (13), *97*
Barnes, F. W., Jr., 132 (3), *133*
Beccari, E., 124 (4), *133*
Behre, J. A., 55 (3), *59*, 124, *133*
Benedict, S. R., *55* (3), *59*, 62 (2), *64*, 124, *133*
Berg, B. N., 50 (6), *54*
Berglund, H., 129 (35), *134*
Bernhard, A., 131 (6), 132 (6), *133*
Bessey, O. A., 82 (8), *83*
Birbraer, M. I., 124 (7), *133*
Blankenstein, A., 124 (8), *133*
Blauch, M. B., 124 (9), 128 (9), 131, *133*
Blecha, E., 52 (11), *54*
Bloch, K., 50, 52 (15), *54*
Block, W. D., 124 (10), 131, *133*
Bodansky, A., 82 (6), *83*
Boivin, A., 123 (11), *133*
Borek, E., 52 (14), *54*
Borsook, H., 124, *134*
Brachet, J., 82 (9), *83*
Brock, M. J., 82 (8), *83*
Brøhner-Mortensen, K., 131, 133 (12), *133*

Brouwer, S. W., 114 (6), *117*
Brown, H., *123*, 125, 131, *133*
Brown, R. K., 95 (13), *97*
Brugnatelli, A., 123, *133*
Brunel, A., 124 (37), *134*
Bulger, H. A., 124 (15), 131, *133*
Burger, M., 133 (16), *133*
Burian, R., 131 (17), *133*
Burstein, L. S., 52 (16), *54*

C

Cadden, J. F., 132 (18), *133*
Calvery, E., 95 (11), *97*
Campbell, W. R., 95, *97*
Cantarow, A., 80 (4), *83*
Chaikoff, I. L., 52 (16, 17), *54*
Chapman, C. B., 52 (12), 54 (12), *54*
Chargaff, E., 113 (2), *117*
Chase, A. F., 132 (27), 133 (27), *134*
Chernick, S. S., 52 (17), *54*
Cherry, I. S., 72 (1), *73*
Christman, A. A., 124, *133*
Ciocalteu, V., 75, *83*, 114 (8), *117*
Clark, E. P., *16*
Clark, L. C., *55* (5), *59*
Claudius, M., 124 (20), *133*
Cohen, H. R., 84, 86, *87*
Cohen, P. P., 113 (3), *117*
Cohn, C., 95, *97*, 133 (86), *135*
Cohn, E. J., 95, *97*
Collip, J. B., *16*
Colvert, J. R., 114 (6), *117*
Comfort, M. W., 72 (2), *73*
Conway, C. F., 131 (88), *135*
Coolidge, T. B., 11 (4), *15*
Coombs, F. S., 133 (76), *135*
Coste, F., 128 (21), *133*
Crandall, L. A., Jr., 72 (1), *73*
Crandall, W. A., 131 (88), *135*

137

138 AUTHOR INDEX

Crawford, J. L., 132 (69), *135*
Cullen, G. E., *19*, *23*, 32

D

Danet, R., 124 (22), *133*
David, M. M., 95, *97*
de Graveve, P., 124 (37), *134*
Delory, G. E., 82 (11), *83*
Denis, W., 129 (34), 132 (23, 34), *133*, *134*
Derick, C., 129 (35), *134*
Derouaux, G., 95 (13), *97*
Dole, V. P., 94 (6), *97*
Dubin, A., 133 (61), *134*
Ducci, H., 11 (6), *15*, 116 (9) *117*

E

Eisenbrand, J., 125 (24), *133*
Elliott, H., 52 (21, 22), *54*
Emerson, K., 94 (6), *97*
Epstein, J., *71*
Evans, M., 55 (4), *59*
Evelyn, K. A., *11*, 14, *15*

F

Falcone, A. B., 14 (7), 15 (7), *15*
Farber, S., 72 (3), *73*
Farr, A. L., 94, *97*
Fearon, W. R., 124 (25), *133*
Feigl, J., 11 (2), *15*
Feinblatt, H. M., 132 (26), 133 (26), *133*
Fine, M. S., 132 (27, 60), 133 (27), *134*
Fischer, E., 124 (28, 29), *134*
Fishberg, A. M., 132 (30), *134*
Fiske, C. H., 84, 86, *87*
Fleury, P., 123 (31), *134*
Flotow, L., 124 (32), *134*
Folin, O., *60*, *64*, 75, *83*, 114 (8), *117*, 119, *122*, 123 (36), 125, 129 (33, 34, 35, 36), 131, 132 (34), *134*
Folley, S. J., 82 (12), *83*
Fosse, R., 124 (37), *134*
Fuller, 62 (3), *64*

G

Gaebler, O. H., 55 (2), *59*
Ganassini, D., 123 (38), 124 (34), *134*
Garn, S. M., 52 (13, 18), *54*
Garry, R. C., 131 (39), *134*
Geib, N. C., 124 (10), 131, *133*
Genevois, P., 123 (31), *134*
Gentzkow, C. F., 119 (1), *122*

Gertler, M. M., 52 (13, 18), *54*
Gillespie, J. M., 95 (13), *97*
Gilman, L., *88*
Giordano, G. G., 131 (40), *134*
Gofman, J. W., 52 (21, 22), *54*
Goldstein, N. P., *71*
Gomori, G., *84*
Gornall, A. G., 95, *97*
Gottfried, S. P., 119 (2), *122*
Grigaut, A., 128 (21), *133*
Grishman, E., 133 (1), *133*
Grzycki, S., 131 (59), *134*
Gurd, F. R. N., 95 (13), *97*
Gutman, A. B., 76 (3), *83*
Gutman, E. B., 76 (3), *83*

H

Hadjioloff, A., 125 (41), *134*
Hamilton, P. B., 94 (6), *97*
Hanger, F., 113 (2), *117*
Hanna, M. I., 95, *97*
Hanson, M., 14 (7), 15 (7), *15*
Harding, V. J., 132 (42), *134*
Haskins, H. D., 132 (43), *134*
Hawk, P. B., 63 (5), *64*, 133 (71), *135*
Hayes, E. R., 50, *54*
Herring, V., 52 (21), *54*
Hewitt, J., 52 (21), *54*
Hill, E., 14 (7), 15 (7), *15*
Hiller, A., 93, 94, *97*
Hoagland, C. L., *113*, 114 (7), 115 (7), *117*
Hoffman, W. S., 133 (61), *134*
Hogden, C. G., 94, *97*
Holbrook, W. P., 132 (43), *134*
Howe, P. C., 88, *97*
Huerga, J. de la, 114 (5), *117*
Hunter, G., 11 (5), *15*
Hupmann, G., 124 (29), *134*
Hutchinson, M. C., 95, *97*

I

Ionescu, M., 124 (44), *134*
Isaacs, R., 132 (45), *134*

J

Jacobson, B. M., 131, 132 (46), 133 (46), *134*
Jaffe, M., 55, *59*
Jankowski, H., 131 (59), *134*
Jansen, A. P., 57 (6), *59*
Johns, H. E., 124 (15), 131, *133*

Johnsson, T., *19*
Johnston, C., 132 (47), *134*
Jones, H. B., 52 (22), *54*
Jones, L. M., 82 (10), 83 (10), *83*

K

Kahnt, F. W., 95 (13), *97*
Kalckar, H. M., 125 (49), *134*
Kallos, J., 124 (48), *134*
Karr, W. G., 63, *64*
Kay, H. D., 82 (12), *83*
Keighley, G., 124, *134*
Kern, A., 124 (51), *134*
Keys, A., 50, 52 (12), 54, *54*
King, E. J., *75*, 76 (2), 82 (11), *83*
Kingsbury, F. B., 132 (52), *134*
Kingsley, G. R., 58 (7), *59*, 88, *97*
Kirk, E., 50, *54*
Koch, F. C., 120, *122*, 124 (9), 131, *133*
Kollmann, G., 132 (53), *134*
Kramer, B., *16*
Kresteff, T., 125 (41), *134*
Krupski, A., 124 (54), *134*
Kunkel, H. G., 94, *97*, 113 (4), *117*
Kuttner, T. T., 84, 86, *87*

L

Langley, W. D., 55 (4), *59*
Leone, E., 124 (55), 131, *134*
Leroy, D., 125 (75), *135*
Lever, W. F., 95 (13), *97*
Lewis, W. H., 50, *54*
Liebig, J., 123 (85), *135*
Lindgren, F., 52 (21, 22), *54*
Liu, C. H., 95 (13), *97*
Lobitz, W. C., 131 (56), *134*
Lowry, O. H., 82 (8), *83*, 94, *97*
Lyon, T. P., 52 (21, 22), *54*

M

MacLagan, N. F., 113 (1), *117*
Maclay, Elizabeth, 86 (3), *87*
McMeekin, T. L., 120, *122*
Maddock, C. L., 72 (3), *73*
Majoor, C. E. H., 88, *97*
Malloy, H. T., *11*, 14, *15*
Mantz, W., 52 (21), *54*
Manzi, G., 124 (55), 131, *134*
Marenzi, A. D., 123 (36), 129 (36), *134*
Martini, A., 124 (57), *134*
Mason, H. L., 131 (56), *134*

Mateer, J. G., 114 (6), *117*
Mayer, A. M., 119 (2), *122*
Mickelsen, O., 50, 52 (12), 54 (12), *54*
Miller, E. v. O., 50, 52 (12), 54 (12), *54*
Milne, J., 88, *97*
Mittelman, D., 95 (13), *97*
Montequi, F., 124 (58), *134*
Moreton, J. R., 52 (19), *54*
Mouton, R. F., 95 (13), *97*
Müller, E., 52 (20), *54*
Myers, V. C., 132 (60), *134*

N

Natelson, S., 112, *112*
Neill, J. M., *23*, 28, *33*
Nelson, N., *65*
Noyons, E. C., 57 (6), *59*

O

Oser, B., 63 (5), *64*
Osterberg, A. E., 72 (2), *73*

P

Page, I. H., 50, *54*
Pascale, L. R., 133 (61), *134*
Peters, J. P., *36*, 51 (10), 52 (10), 53 (10), *54*
Phillips, R. A., 94, *97*
Pillemer, L., 95, *97*
Pitarelli, E., 124 (62), *134*
Plazin, J., 93, 94, *97*
Plentl, A. A., 131 (63), *134*
Polakoff, P. P., Jr., 72 (4), 73 (6, 7), *74*
Popesco, A., 124 (44), *134*
Popper, H., 114 (5), *117*

Q

Querner, E., 11 (2), *15*

R

Rabinowitch, I. M., 132 (64), 133 (64), *134*
Randall, R. J., 94, *97*
Ravwitsch, S., 124, *133*
Recant, L., 113 (2), *117*
Reiche, F. Z., 131 (65), *134*
Reimer, A., 52 (11), *54*
Reiner, M., *36*
Reinhart, H. L., 82 (10), 83 (10), *83*
Reinhold, J. G., 88
Rittenberg, D., 50, 52 (14), *54*

Subject Index